Questions and Answers

PHYSICS

KEY STAGE 4

Graham Booth & Bob McDuell

Chief Examiners

SERIES EDITOR: BOB McDUELL

Contents

HOW TO USE THIS BOOK

The aim of the *Questions and Answers* series is to provide students with the help required to attain the highest level of achievement in one of their most important examinations – the General Certificate of Secondary Education (GCSE) or, in Scotland, at General and Credit levels. The books are designed to help all students, up to and including A* grade at GCSE. The series relies on the premise that an experienced Examiner can provide, through examination questions, sample answers and advice, the help students need to secure success. Many revision aids concentrate on providing factual information which might have to be recalled in an examination. This series, while giving factual information in an easy-to-remember form, concentrates on the other skills which need to be developed for new GCSE examinations.

Students often find it useful to plan their revision according to some predetermined pattern, during which weaknesses can be identified and eliminated so that their confidence can grow. Because of this, our primary consideration has been to present the main principles on which study can be based.

The *Questions and Answers* series is designed to provide:

- Easy-to-use **Revision Summaries** which identify important factual information. These are to remind you, in summary form, of the topics you will need to have revised in order to answer exam questions.
- Advice on the different types of question in each subject and how to answer them well to obtain the highest marks.
- Information about other skills, apart from the recall of knowledge, that will be tested on examination papers. These are sometimes called **Assessment Objectives**. Modern GCSE examinations put great emphasis on the testing of objectives other than knowledge and understanding. Typically, questions testing these Assessment Objectives can make up 50% of the mark allocated to the written papers. Assessment Objectives include communication, problem solving, evaluation and interpretation. The *Questions and Answers* series is intended to develop these skills by the use of questions and showing how marks are allocated.
- Many examples of **examination questions**, with spaces for you to fill in your answers, just as on an examination paper. Students can improve by studying a sufficiently wide range of questions, providing they are shown the way to improve their answers to these questions. It is advisable that students try these questions first before going to the answers and the advice which accompanies the answers. Some of the questions come from actual examination papers or specimen materials issued by Examination Boards. Other questions have been written to mirror closely these questions. The writing has been done by Chief Examiners who write questions for Examination Boards. The questions meet the requirements of all British Examination Boards.
- **Sample answers** to all of the questions.
- **Advice from Examiners**. By using the experience of actual Chief Examiners we are able to give advice which can enable students to see how their answers can be improved and success ensured.

Success in GCSE examinations comes from proper preparation and a positive attitude to the examination, developed through a sound knowledge of facts and an understanding of principles. These books are intended to overcome 'examination nerves' which often come from a fear of not being properly prepared.

DEVISING A REVISION PLAN

The importance of beginning your revision well in advance of your examination cannot be overemphasized. You will obtain a fair idea of your memory capacity by reading part of a text which is new to you and, after 40 minutes, writing out how many facts you can remember. The average person will recall about 50%, then after an interval of 10 minutes, 25% of the original material will be remembered. After two days you will probably recall no more than 15%. These are average figures, of course, so do not be depressed if your scores are lower or complacent if they are higher. Your capacity for retention will be influenced by the amount of sleep that you have had, what other matters are on your mind and your interest in the topic.

The fact that only 15% of the material you learn may be remembered could be depressing and make you wonder whether revision is worthwhile. What is important, however, is that the amount remembered is dramatically increased by revising the original material after one week and then again after two weeks. By this time, the facts will be stored in your so-called long-term memory and up to 80% of the original material should be retained.

You can only maintain concentration for a short period of time and the actual length of time will vary from person to person. Break up your revision into short periods of time, perhaps 30 minutes or so each, and build in short breaks between revision periods. Set yourself a reasonable target for each week – something which you can achieve but will stretch you. Monitor your progress and amend your weekly targets accordingly. Divide the topics to be studied into two lists – topics you need to work on and topics you are happy with. Try to transfer as many as possible from the first list to the second.

DIFFERENT TYPES OF EXAMINATION QUESTION

Structured questions

These are the most common type of question used at GCSE on Physics papers. All of the questions in this book are structured questions. The reason why they are so widely used is that they are so versatile. They can be short with little opportunity for extended writing. In this form they are suitable for use on Basic Level papers. Alternatively, they can be longer and more complex in their structure with opportunities for extended writing and demonstration of the higher level skills of interpretation and evaluation. In this form they are very suitable for Higher Level papers.

In a structured question, the question is divided into parts (a), (b), (c) etc. These parts can be further subdivided into (i), (ii), (iii), (iv) etc. A structure is built into the question and hence into your answer. This is where the term structured question comes from.

For each part of the question there are a number of lines or a space for your answer. This is a guide to you about the detail required in the answer, but it does not have to limit you. If you require more space continue your answer on a separate sheet of paper but make sure you label the answer clearly, e.g. 3(a)(ii).

For each part of the question there is a number in brackets, e.g. (3), to show you how many marks are allocated to this part of the question by the examiner. If a part is worth three marks, for example, the question requires more than one or two words. As a general rule if there are three marks allocated, you will need to make three points.

To give you a guide as you work through structured questions, papers are often designed to enable you to score one mark per minute. A question worth a maximum of 15 marks should therefore take about 15 minutes to answer.

You do not have to write your answers in full sentences. Concise notes are often the most suitable response. Remember you are eligible for up to an extra 5% for the quality of your spelling, punctuation and grammar (SPAG). These marks are gained especially for the use of technical words correctly spelt and used accurately. It is very important, if you have time at the end of the examination, to check your answers both for accuracy in answering the questions and for spelling, correct use of punctuation (full stops and apostrophes, in particular) and grammatical mistakes. Read your answers to yourself, not aloud, and check that they make sense.

It is most important to read the stimulus material in the question thoroughly and more than once. This information is often not used fully by students and, as a result, the question is not answered fully. The key to answering many of these questions comes from the appreciation of the full meaning of the 'command word' at the start of the question – 'state, describe, explain'. The following glossary of command words may help you in the answering of structured questions

- **State** This means a brief answer is required with no supporting evidence. Alternatives include **write down**, **give**, **list**, **name**.
- **Define** Just a definition is required.
- **State and explain** A short answer is required (see **state**) but then an explanation is required. A question of this type should be worth more than one mark.
- **Describe** This is often used with reference to a particular experiment. The important points should be given about each stage. Again this type of question is worth more than one mark.
- **Outline** The answer should be brief and the main points picked out.
- **Predict** A brief answer is required without supporting evidence. You are required to make logical links between various pieces of information.
- **Complete** You are required to add information to a diagram, sentence, flow chart, graph, key, table, etc.
- **Find** This is a general term which may mean calculate, measure, determine, etc.
- **Calculate** A numerical answer is required. You should show your working in order to get an answer. Do not forget the correct units.
- **Suggest** There is not just one correct answer or you are applying your answer to a situation outside the syllabus.

Free response questions

These can include essay questions. In this type of question you are given a question which enables you to develop your answer in different ways. Your answer really is a free response and you write as much as you wish. Candidates often do not write enough or try to 'pad out' the answer. Remember you can only score marks when your answer matches the marking points on the examiner's marking scheme.

In this type of question it is important to plan your answer before starting it, allocating the correct amount of time to each part of the question. Again attention to spelling, punctuation and grammar is important.

Sample question

Choose one part of the electromagnetic spectrum. Describe one use of the waves in that part of the spectrum. Explain how the properties of the waves make them suitable for the use that you have described. (6)

Describe how the waves you have chosen fit into the electromagnetic spectrum. (3)

This question should take about 10–15 minutes to answer. In preparation you need to consider which part of the spectrum to choose; it is a good idea to choose a part of the spectrum that you know something about and can give an example of a use. There is no mark for choosing the waves.

Plan Choose X-rays and describe their use to examine broken bones. Include absorption or transmission through flesh or bone.

Here is a sample answer.

X-rays can be used to examine parts of the body for bone fractures.

[1 mark for knowing a use for X-rays]

The X-ray beam is passed through part of a person's leg, for example, and detected by a photographic film placed behind the leg.

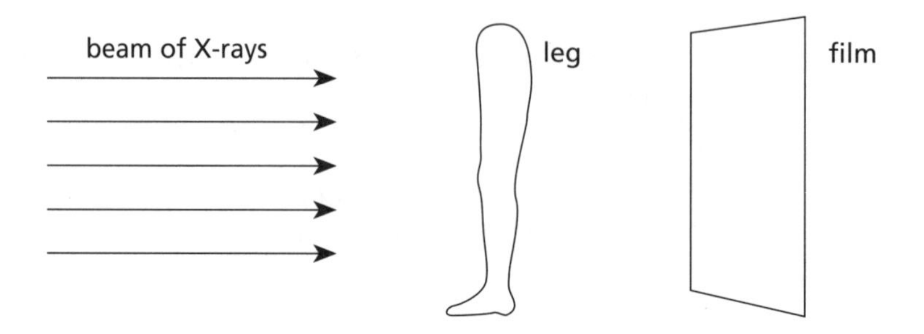

[It is a good idea to use freehand sketches to help to describe a situation or explain a meaning. This helps the examiner who is marking your paper because it makes your answer clearer. There are two marks awarded here; one for knowing that X-rays can be detected by photographic film and one for knowing where the film is placed in relation to the leg and the X-ray beam.]

X-rays are absorbed by bone but pass easily through flesh.

[This statement contains two properties of X-rays that make it suitable for the use being described. Each of these properties gains one mark. For the final mark, we need to add the detail of how the fracture is detected.]

A fracture in the bone shows on the X-ray plate as a dark line because the X-rays have passed through it and affected the plate.

Now for the second part of the question.

X-rays are short-wavelength waves.

[1 mark for knowing whereabouts in the spectrum X-rays occur. The question asks how they fit into the spectrum, so for the final two marks two comparisons will be made.]

They have a longer wavelength than gamma rays and a shorter wavelength than ultra-violet waves.

ASSESSMENT OBJECTIVES IN PHYSICS

Assessment Objectives are the intellectual and practical skills you should be able to show. Opportunities must be made by the Examiner when setting the examination paper for you to demonstrate your mastery of these skills when you answer the question paper.

Traditionally the Assessment Objective of knowledge and understanding has been regarded as the most important skill to develop. Candidates have been directed to learn large bodies of knowledge to recall in the examination. Whilst not wanting in any way to devalue the learning of facts, it should be remembered that on modern papers knowledge and understanding can only contribute about half of the marks available. The other half of the marks are acquired by mastery of the other Assessment Objectives namely:

- Communicate scientific observations, ideas and arguments effectively.
- Select and use reference materials and translate data from one form to another.
- Interpret, evaluate and make informed judgements from relevant facts, observations and phenomena.
- Solve qualitative and quantitative problems.

1 Communicate scientific observations, ideas and arguments effectively

(*weighting on papers approximately 5–10%*)

In any examination, communication of information to the examiner is of primary importance. This Assessment Objective should not be confused with spelling, punctuation and grammar (SPAG) — up to 5% added to your mark on the paper for the quality of your spelling, punctuation and grammar.

Questions are built into the paper to test you ability to communicate scientific information. Often these questions require extended answers.

In this type of question it is important to look at your answer objectively after you have written it and try to judge whether your answer is communicating information effectively.

2 Select and use reference materials and translate data from one form to another (*weighting on papers approximately 10–15%*)

In questions testing this Assessment Objective you are asked frequently to pick information from a chart or table and use it in another form, e.g. to draw a graph, a pie chart, bar chart, etc. You may be asked to complete a table using information from a graph.

It is important to transfer the skills you have acquired in Mathematics to your work in Physics.

Skill acquired	Approx. grade in GCSE Maths
Read information from graphs or simple diagrams	F
Work out simple percentages	F
Construct and use pie charts	F
Use graphs	E
Plot graphs from data provided. The axes and scales are given to you.	E
Be able to draw the best line through points on a graph	C
Select the most appropriate axes and scales for graph plotting	B

It is reasonable, therefore, to conclude that at Higher level, you might be required to use a blank piece of graph paper and choose your own scales and axes. Then you would plot the points and draw a line of best fit through the points. If you are doing this, remember:

❶ To draw your graph as large as possible on the graph paper by choosing scales appropriately. Avoid choosing scales where, for example, 3 small squares are equivalent to 5°C. It would be better if 1 small square was equivalent to 1°C or 2 °C. With this type of graph drawing, marks are usually awarded for the choice of scales and for labelled axes.

❷ To plot each point with a dot or small cross. Circle the dot or cross to make its position clear.

❸ Your line of best fit, whether it is a straight line or a curve, does not have to go through all the points. Some points may not be in the correct place, even if you plotted them correctly, because of inaccuracies in the experiment or experimental error.

On a Central tier paper a similar graph may have to be drawn but it would be more appropriate for the examiner to provide a grid with axes and scales given. Then you would only have to plot the points and draw the line of best fit. It would probably be worth less marks than a graph on the Higher tier paper.

3 Interpret, evaluate and make informed judgements from relevant facts, observations and phenomena (*weighting on papers approximately 10–15%*)

Questions testing this Assessment Objective are often difficult for candidates. It is much easier to test this on a Higher tier paper than on a Basic tier paper.

The command word 'suggest' is very frequently used as the information given, perhaps in a paragraph, table, diagram or any combination of these, is open to more than one interpretation.

Look carefully at all of the information given and look for possible alternative interpretations before writing your answer.

4 Solve qualitative and quantitative problems (*weighting on papers approximately 10–15%*)

There is no shortage of opportunities to ask questions testing this Assessment Objective on Physics GCSE papers. Again opportunities are greater, especially for solving quantitative problems, on Higher tier papers.

Qualitative problems can include describing energy transfers or explaining how conservation of energy applies to an energy transfer. Quantitative problems include the full range of physical calculations which have baffled students studying Physics for generations. Remember, when attempting to carry out a physical calculation, to:

❶ Use all of the information given to you. If the question gives specific heat capacities, they should be used.

❷ Show all of your working so credit can be given if you do not get the correct answer but get some way through the question.

❸ Take care when substituting in a mathematical formula to be consistent in your units.

❹ Give correct units to your answers if there are units. Remember ratios, including efficiencies, do not have units.

You will see questions throughout this book where the question is designed to test Assessment Objectives other than knowledge and understanding.

Formulae that you should know

This is a list of formulae that you may need to use in answering Physics questions but will not be given to you either on the examination paper or on a separate formula sheet.

For Basic tier papers:

pressure = force ÷ area $p = \dfrac{F}{A}$

speed = distance ÷ time taken $v = \dfrac{d}{t}$

In addition, for Central tier papers:

$\dfrac{\text{pressure}_1 \times \text{volume}_1}{\text{temperature}_1} = \dfrac{\text{pressure}_2 \times \text{volume}_2}{\text{temperature}_2}$ $\dfrac{p_1V_1}{T_1} = \dfrac{p_2V_2}{T_2}$

work done = force × distance moved in its own direction $W = Fd$

power = energy transferred or work done ÷ time taken $P = \dfrac{E}{t}$

moment of a force = size of force × perpendicular distance from force to pivot

in a balanced system,
the sum of clockwise moments about a point = the sum of the anticlockwise moments about that point

energy = potential difference × current × time $E = VIt$

energy change = mass × specific heat capacity × change in temperature $E = mc\Delta T$

force = mass × acceleration $F = ma$

acceleration = increase in velocity ÷ time taken $a = \dfrac{v}{t}$

wave speed = frequency × wavelength $v = f\lambda$

In addition, for Further tier papers:

charge = current × time $Q = It$

potential difference = current × resistance $V = IR$

power = potential difference × current $P = VI$

weight = mass × gravitational field strength $w = mg$

kinetic energy = $1/2$ × mass × (speed)^2 ke = $1/2mv^2$

change in gravitational potential energy =
mass × gravitational field strength × change in height gpe = $mg\Delta h$

momentum = mass × velocity $p = mv$

1 Electricity and magnetism

REVISION SUMMARY

Logic gates are electronically operated switches. With the exception of the NOT gate, most common logic gates have two inputs. The name of the gate describes the conditions of the inputs for the output to be 'on', or at logic 1.

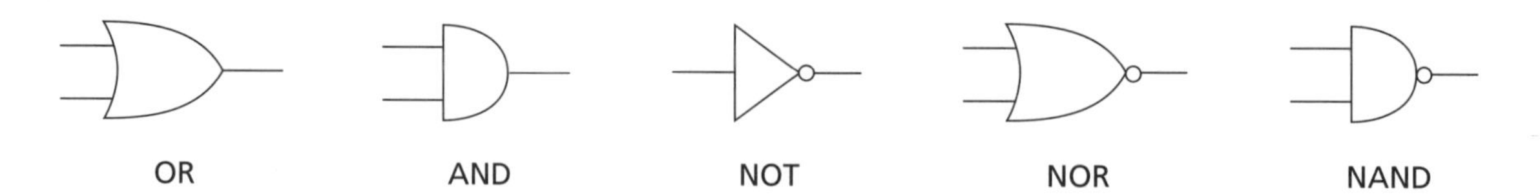

Note that **NOR** stands for **NOT OR**; it is the same as an **OR** gate followed by a **NOT**. Similarly, **NAND** acts as an **AND** gate followed by a **NOT**.

Logic gates are often used with sensors such as light, temperature and moisture sensors to switch things on or off according to environmental conditions. These electronic systems often involve the use of **feedback**, where the output of the system feeds back to the input. An example of this is temperature control.

Useful circuits can be made by combining logic gates. The **bistable** circuit is a memory circuit; it 'remembers' the input signal (either 0 or 1) even when that input has been removed. The diagram represents a bistable unit.

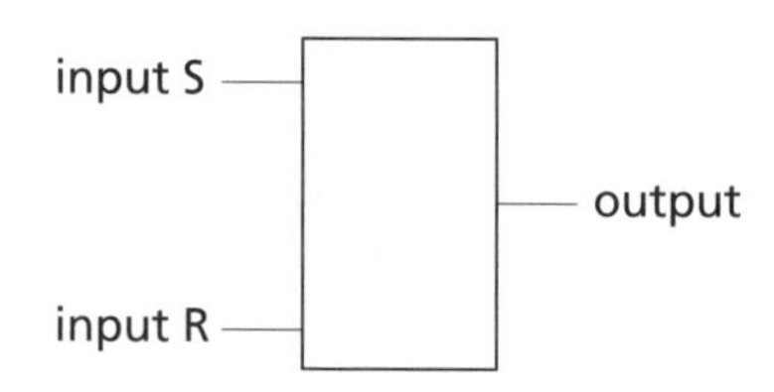

The **binary digit** (0 or 1) which is to be remembered is applied to the **S** (or **set**) input and this appears at the output. The output then keeps that value even when the input value is changed or removed. The **R** input is to **reset** the bistable so that it is ready to remember another digit. As well as being used in large numbers in computer memories, bistable circuits have applications as latches in circuits such as burglar alarms.

The amount of electric **current** passing in a circuit depends on the **potential difference**, or voltage, and the **resistance**. Increasing the voltage applies a bigger force to the moving charges, giving a greater flow. **Resistance** is the opposition to the electric current; more resistance in a circuit reduces the current passing.

The formula for calculating resistance is:

$$\text{resistance} = \frac{\text{potential difference}}{\text{current}} \quad \text{or in symbols} \quad R = \frac{V}{I}$$

Resistance is measured in **ohms** (symbol Ω).

The job of a circuit is to transfer **energy** from the source, battery or power supply, to the components – lamps, heater, motors and other devices.

Potential difference, or voltage, is a measure of the energy transfer. A 12V power supply transfers 12 **joules** of energy to each **coulomb** of charge. When the charge flows through a lamp the energy is transferred into heat energy and light energy. So potential difference measures energy transfer both ways – the p.d. across a power supply measures the electrical energy transfer **into** the circuit and the p.d. across a component measures the energy transfer **from** electrical energy.

Power measures the energy transfer each second; this is determined by both the current and the potential difference.

REVISION SUMMARY

The following equations show the relationships between current, charge, power and potential difference:

$$\text{current (in A)} = \frac{\text{charge flow (in C)}}{\text{time (in s)}}$$

$$\text{potential difference (in V)} = \frac{\text{energy transfer (in J)}}{\text{charge (in C)}}$$

$$\text{power (in W)} = \text{p.d. (in V)} \times \text{current (in A)}$$

Written in symbols, these are:

$$I = \frac{Q}{t} \qquad V = \frac{E}{Q} \qquad P = IV$$

Electric currents also have **magnetic fields**; this is called **electromagnetism** and is used in devices such as relays (electromagnetic switches), motors and loudspeakers to produce movement.

Electromagnetic induction is the name given to the way in which electrical energy is generated and transformed. In a generator or bicycle dynamo a magnet rotates inside a coil of wire. The changing magnetic field causes a voltage to be induced; the size of the **induced voltage** depends on the **rate** at which the magnetic field changes.

Transformers are efficient devices which use electromagnetism for changing the size of an alternating voltage. The equation for this is:

$$\frac{\text{number of turns on primary coil}}{\text{number of turns on secondary coil}} = \frac{\text{primary voltage}}{\text{secondary voltage}}$$

Transformers do not give a free supply of energy; when used to increase the voltage they reduce the current and they give increased currents when the voltage is reduced.

$$\frac{\text{number of turns on primary coil}}{\text{number of turns on secondary coil}} = \frac{\text{secondary current}}{\text{primary current}}$$

The electricity supply industry makes extensive use of transformers; transmitting energy at high voltages enables low currents to be used which reduces the energy losses in transmission. Transformers **step up** the voltage at the power station before the energy is fed into the grid and **step down** the voltage in several stages before the energy is delivered to homes, commerce and industry.

The **joule** is too small a unit for measuring the energy supplied to homes so the electricity supply industry uses the **kilowatt hour**. The energy transferred is calculated using the formula:

$$\text{energy (in kWh)} = \text{power (in kW)} \times \text{time (in h)}$$

Electric appliances need to be fitted with safety features to reduce the risk of fire and electrocution. **Fuses** fitted in the consumer unit (or fuse box) should cut off the current if it reaches such a level that the wiring cables are in danger of overheating and setting on fire. In a similar way, fuses fitted to plugs protect from fire hazard. The fuse wire melts and this stops the current if there is a fault that causes a larger than normal current to pass. **Earth** wires should be connected to the casing of any appliance that has a metal case. Should the case become 'live' a large current then passes to earth which 'blows' the fuse and cuts off the electrical supply.

Televisions and X-ray tubes both use high-speed beams of electrons produced by **thermionic emission**. In televisions the electron beam is directed to the desired part of the screen where it strikes fluorescent materials called phosphors. These convert some of the kinetic energy of the moving electrons into electromagnetic radiation in the visible spectrum, or light energy. X-ray tubes use higher-energy electron beams which are fired at a metal target. The electromagnetic radiation produced has a higher energy than that from the phosphors in a television tube. This high-energy radiation is in the short wavelength part of the electromagnetic spectrum.

If you need to revise this subject more thoroughly, see the relevant topics in the Letts GCSE *Physics Study Guide.*

QUESTIONS

1 A burglar alarm is operated by three switches. Switches A and B are fitted to two separate doors and switch M is the master switch. When a door is opened or the master switch is turned on it causes the input to a logic gate to be 'on'. The diagram shows the circuit which is used.

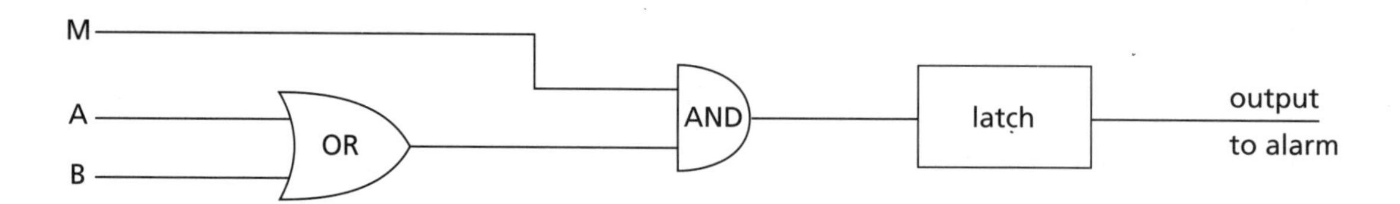

(a) Complete the table using a 0 for 'off' and a 1 for 'on'.

	inputs to OR gate		inputs to AND gate		
	A	**B**	**OR gate output**	**M**	**AND gate output**
i	0	0	0	1	0
ii	1	0	1	1	1
iii	0	1	1	0	0
iv	1	1	1	0	0

(4)

(b) Which line of the table shows what happens when the master switch is 'on' and the doors are closed?

.... (1)

(c) Which lines of the table show what happens when a door is opened while the master switch is 'off'?

.... (1)

(d) Describe what has to happen for the alarm to sound.

....

....

.... (2)

(e) Explain the purpose of the latch.

....

.... (2)

QUESTIONS

2 A student compares three different metal wires to see which is the best conductor of electricity. He passes a current of 0.8 A in each wire in turn and measures the potential difference needed. The table shows his results.

wire	potential difference/V
A	5.2
B	0.6
C	12.4

(a) Which wire is the best conductor of electricity? Explain your choice.

....

.... (2)

(b) Calculate the resistance of wire A.

....

....

.... (3)

(c) While doing the experiment, the student notices that one of the wires gets hot. Calculate the power in each wire and use your answers to explain which wire gets hot.

....

....

....

....

.... (5)

(d) Calculate the quantity of electric charge which passes through each wire in one minute.

....

....

.... (3)

QUESTIONS

3 (a) The diagram shows two circuits.

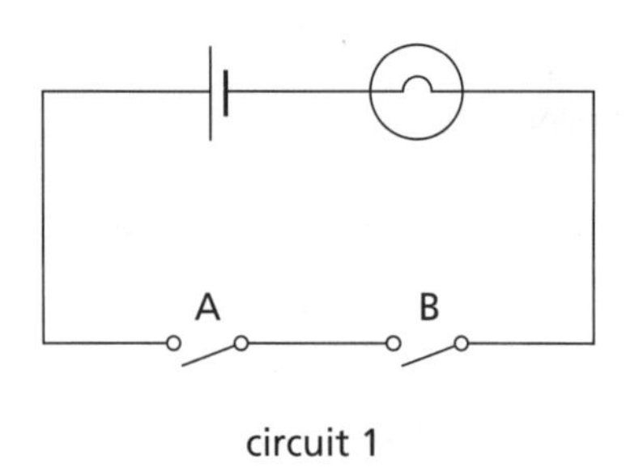

circuit 1

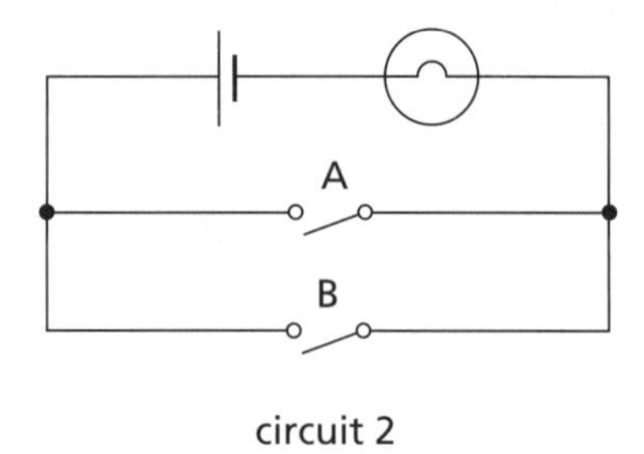

circuit 2

Complete the sentences.

In circuit 1, for the lamp to be on A ______ B must be on.

In circuit 2, for the lamp to be on A ______ B must be on. (2)

(b) Describe the job of the variable resistor in each of the following circuits. (2)

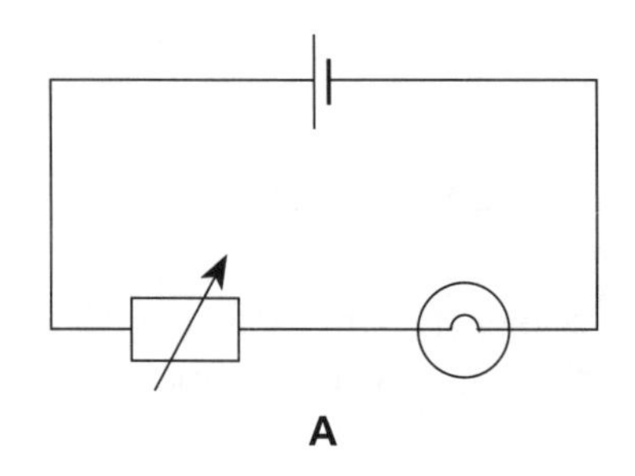
A

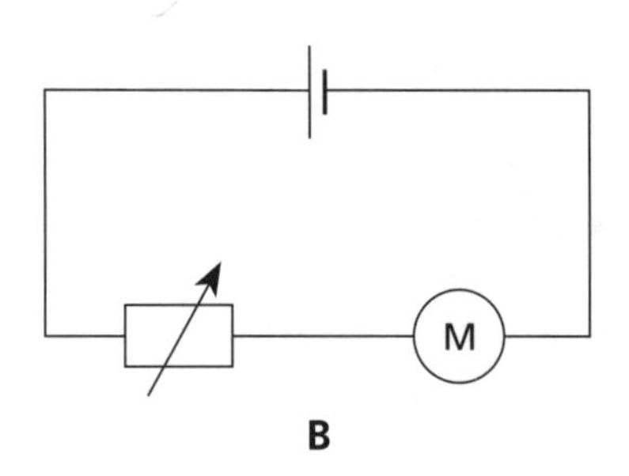

B

In circuit A the variable resistor ....

....

In circuit B the variable resistor ....

....

(c) Draw a diagram of a circuit with a switch, a lamp and a motor so that the lamp is on only when the motor is on. (3)

(d) Draw a diagram of a circuit with a lamp, a motor and a variable resistor that controls the speed of the motor but does not affect the lamp. (3)

4 The diagram represents a vertical wire passing through a piece of stiff card which is horizontal. The arrow shows the direction of the electric current in the wire.

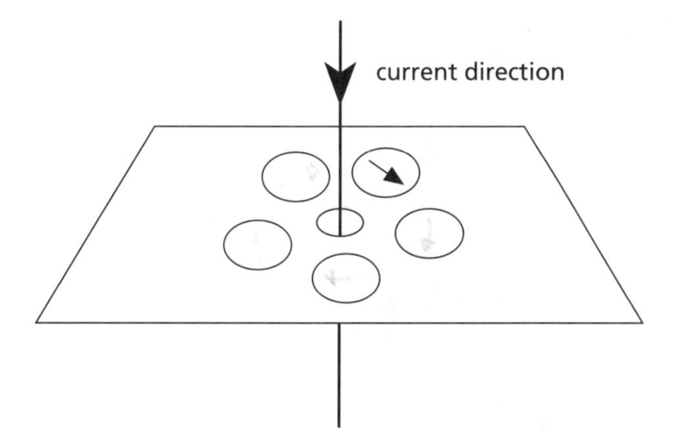

(a) Five small compasses have been placed around the wire so that the magnetic field can be studied. Complete the diagram by drawing in the other four compass needles. (2)

(b) The magnetic field due to a single wire is weak, even when a large current passes in the wire. Describe two ways in which the magnetic field can be made stronger.

....

.... (2)

(c) A relay is a switch which is operated when current passes in a coil of wire. The diagram shows a relay.

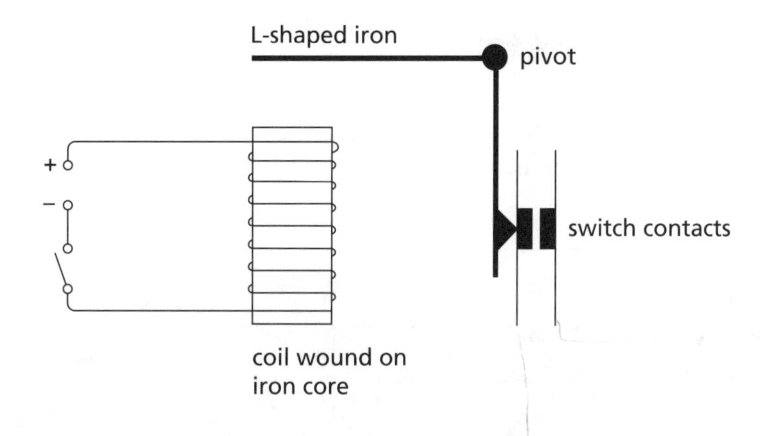

QUESTIONS

Describe and explain what happens when a current passes in the coil.

....

....

....

.... (4)

(d) Complete the circuit diagram to show how to connect a mains lamp which can be switched on and off by the relay. (2)

5 The diagram shows a magnet and a coil of wire which is connected to a sensitive ammeter. When the magnet is moved slowly into the coil the needle on the ammeter shows a steady deflection to the right.

N S

sensitive ammeter

(a) Explain why there is a reading on the ammeter when the magnet is moved into the coil.

....

.... (2)

(b) Describe and explain the ammeter reading when the magnet is:

(i) held steady inside the coil

....

.... (2)

(ii) withdrawn slowly from the coil

....

.... (2)

(iii) moved quickly in and out of the coil

....

.... (2)

6 A power station produces electricity at 25 000 volts. This voltage is stepped up to 400 000 volts by a transformer.

400 000 volts

transformer

power station

25 000 volts

(a) The number of turns on the primary coil of the transformer is 20 000. Calculate the number of turns on the secondary coil.

....

.... (2)

(b) Why is a voltage as high as 400 000 volts used in the transmission of electrical energy?

.... (1)

SEB 1994

7 The diagram shows a circuit which can be used to control the brightness of a lamp.

240 V

fuse

(a) State and explain where the sliding contact should be placed for the lamp to be at its brightest.

....

....

.... (3)

QUESTIONS

(b) The maximum power of the lamp is 1000 W. Calculate the current in the filament at this power.

....

....

.... (3)

8 The diagram represents an electronic system which is used to control the temperature in an incubator.

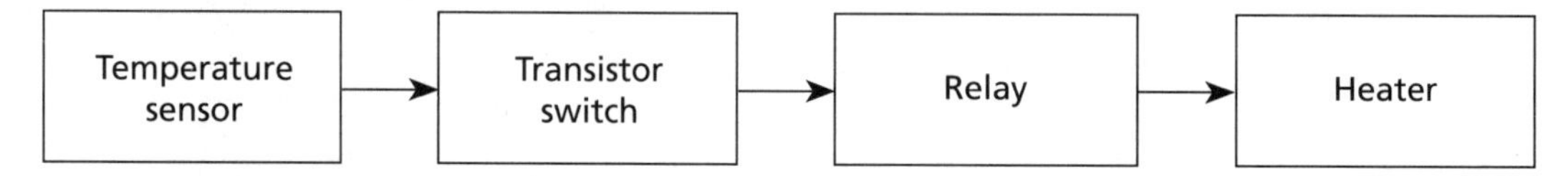

(a) Explain how feedback is used in this system to control the temperature of the incubator.

.... (3)

(b) Explain the purpose of the relay between the transistor switch and the heater.

....

.... (2)

The circuit diagram shows how the temperature sensor is made from a fixed resistor and a thermistor. The resistance of the thermistor decreases when its temperature increases.

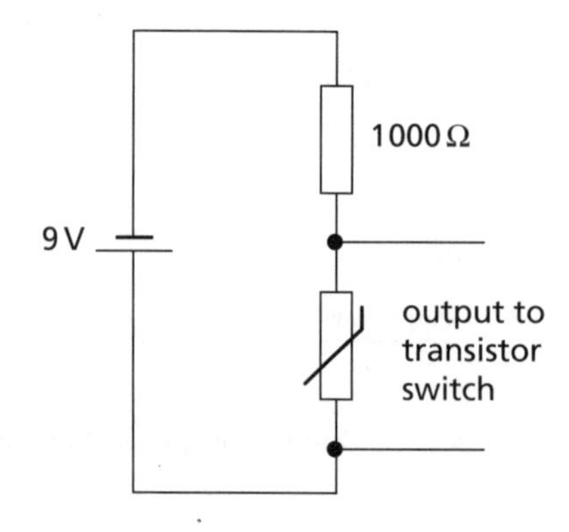

(c) The transistor switch is switched on when the input to it is 0.6 V or more.

(i) Calculate the potential difference across the $1000\,\Omega$ resistor when the potential difference across the thermistor is 0.6 V.

.... (1)

QUESTIONS

(ii) Use your value from (i) to calculate the current in the circuit and the resistance of the thermistor when the potential difference across the thermistor is 0.6 V.

....

....

....

.... (4)

(iii) Suggest why the current in the temperature sensing circuit needs to be low.

....

.... (2)

(d) Explain why the transistor switch turns the heater off when the temperature of the thermistor rises.

....

....

.... (3)

2 Energy resources and energy transfer

REVISION SUMMARY

For an object to have **energy** it must be able to make something happen. Fuels, things on the move, things that have been lifted up, electromagnetic radiation and materials transmitting sound or other vibrations all have energy.
The table lists the different forms of energy and gives a description of each one.

form of energy	description
Kinetic	energy due to movement
Gravitational potential	energy gained when an object is lifted up
Elastic potential	energy stored when an object is stretched or deformed
Sound	energy of the molecules transmitting the sound
Chemical	energy stored by all foods and fuels; released when they are oxidized or undergo other exothermic reaction
Nuclear	released as kinetic energy when a large nucleus splits up (fission) or a small nucleus is created from its constituent particles (fusion)
Thermal (heat)	the energy an object absorbs when its temperature rises and releases when its temperature falls; also absorbed or released when a substance changes state
Light	energy of the visible part of the electromagnetic spectrum
Radiant	this term is sometimes used to describe the energy of any part of the electromagnetic spectrum
Electrical	the energy transferred to charged particles from a source of electricity
Magnetic	the energy in a magnetic field

Energy is constantly being transferred between these different forms. A braking car is transferring **kinetic** energy into **thermal** energy; when it accelerates **chemical** energy from the fuel is being transferred into **kinetic** energy but a car travelling at a constant speed on the level is just transferring **chemical** energy into **thermal** energy of the surroundings!

Devices such as heaters, lamps, television sets and radios are designed to carry out a particular energy transfer; a gas fire is designed to transfer **chemical** energy from the gas into **thermal** energy and a lamp is designed to transfer **electrical** energy into **light** energy. Although all the energy that goes into one of these devices must come out (this is known as **conservation of energy**; the total amount of energy remains the same), it does not all come out in the desired form.

Tungsten filament lamps are poor at achieving the desired energy transfer, typically producing about 5 J of light energy for every 100 J of electrical energy supplied. The rest is emitted as thermal energy. Modern fluorescent lamps are more **efficient**; they transfer more of the energy input into the desired output, i.e. light. The **efficiency** of a device is the fraction or percentage of the energy input that is output in a useful form. Filament lamps have an efficiency of about 5% while that for fluorescent lamps is about 20%.

There are three mechanisms by which thermal energy from hot objects such as lamps and heaters is lost to the surroundings. Everything emits **infra-red radiation**; the rate of emission increases with increasing temperature and also depends on the nature of the surface. A dull, dark surface emits more radiation than a shiny one at the same temperature. The dark surface is also a better absorber than the shiny one; aluminium foil and silvered surfaces are used as insulators because they reflect infra-red radiation so they can reduce the amount leaving a hot object or entering a cold one.

A second mechanism is by **conduction**; the transfer of energy from an energetic molecule to a less energetic one when they collide. Conduction in metals is a more rapid process than in non-metals because the **free electrons** diffuse within the metal, spreading the energy around.

REVISION SUMMARY

The third mechanism is by **convection currents**, which only occur in fluids; they are caused by differences in density when part of the fluid is warmed or cooled. Convection currents keep the air circulating in a refrigerator and in a room that is heated by a 'radiator'.

Energy lost to the surroundings by a hot object cannot be recovered easily. This is because it becomes spread out and raises the temperature of the surroundings by a very small amount. It is not easy to extract energy from a low-temperature source; one way in which it can be done is by using a heat pump. This device is like a refrigerator running in reverse, with the energy absorber (the ice box in a refrigerator) being placed outside, often underground or in a river, and the energy emitter (the cooling pipes at the back of a refrigerator) inside a building.

The amount of energy absorbed or released when an object heats up or cools down depends on the temperature change, the quantity of material and its **specific heat capacity**. The specific heat capacity is the energy transfer needed to change the temperature of 1 kg of material by 1 °C or 1 K. The equation is:

$$\text{energy change} = \text{mass} \times \text{specific heat capacity} \times \text{temperature change}$$

Most of the energy that we transfer in our homes comes from fossil fuels; energy from the Sun was trapped millions of years ago and stored as **chemical** energy. Fossil fuels are **non-renewable**; we cannot make any more coal, gas or oil. Nuclear fission fuels such as uranium are also non-renewable. Some electricity is generated from renewable sources; **hydroelectric** power uses energy from the Sun that drives the water cycle and **wind** power uses energy from the Sun that causes movement of airstreams. Solar cells convert energy from the Sun directly into electrical energy but their high cost and low efficiency give them limited use in the UK.

Our bodies use **renewable** energy sources; plants transfer energy from the Sun into chemical energy; unlike the formation of coal, this is a short-term process and one that can be repeated many times in a short timescale.

Cost is an important factor when choosing an energy source and this is often governed by availability. Environmental factors are increasingly being taken into account but whereas wind 'farms' do not cause the atmospheric pollution associated with fossil fuels, some people regard them as being noisy and ugly. Social factors to be taken into account include employment and environmental changes that could affect tourism or the livelihood of a community.

If you need to revise this subject more thoroughly, see the relevant topics in the Letts *GCSE Physics Study Guide*.

QUESTIONS

1 (a) Some of the jobs listed below involve an energy transfer and some do not. Place a tick at the side of those that involve transfer of energy.

- ☐ a man pushing a supermarket trolley
- ☐ a girl pedalling a bicycle
- ☐ a shelf supporting some books
- ☐ a gas flame heating some water
- ☐ the weight of a building pushing down on the ground
- ☐ water evaporating from the sea
- ☐ the upward push of the sea on a floating ship
- ☐ the upward push of the atmosphere on a rising hot-air balloon (8)

(b) A lamp is **designed** to transfer *electrical energy* into *light energy*. The diagrams show some other devices which transfer energy. Complete the sentences to show the energy transfer that each device is designed for.

A coffee maker is designed to transfer .... energy into .... energy.

A television set is designed to transfer .... energy into .... energy and .... energy.

A bunsen burner is designed to transfer .... energy into .... energy.

(7)

(c) Modern 'energy-efficient' lamps produce the same light output as tungsten filament lamps for less electrical energy input. The following diagram is an incomplete picture of the energy flow through an 'energy-efficient' lamp in one second.

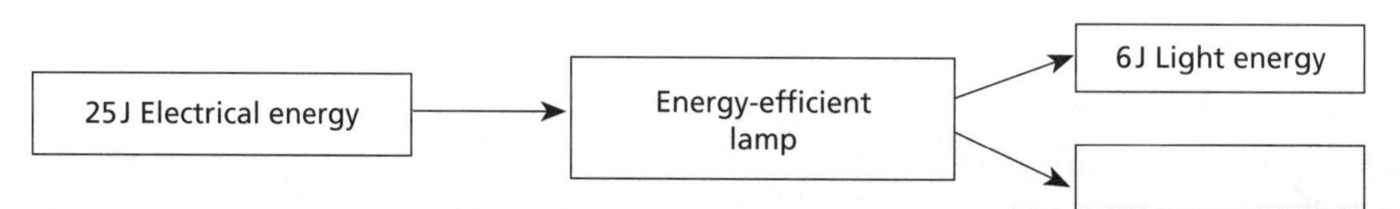

Complete the diagram by writing the amount and type of energy in the blank box. (2)

2 (a) The diagram shows an electric immersion heater in a hot water tank.

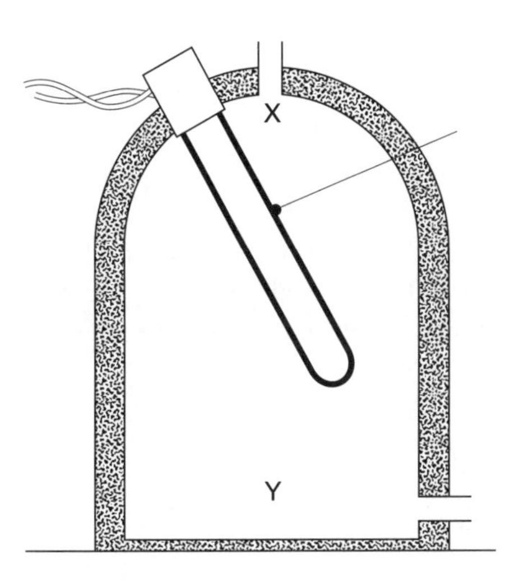

(i) After the heater has been switched on for a short time, the water at X is warm. Describe how the water at X is heated.

....

....

.... (3)

(ii) It takes a long time for the water at Y to become warm. Describe how the energy travels from the heating element to Y and explain why this is a slow process.

....

....

.... (3)

(b) In the water tank, 200 kg of water are heated from 10 °C to 50 °C by the immersion heater. The specific heat capacity of water is $4200\,J\,kg^{-1}\,°C^{-1}$.

(i) Calculate the energy absorbed by the water.

....

....

.... (3)

(ii) Explain why the immersion heater has to provide more energy than the amount calculated in (b)(i).

....

....

.... (2)

(c) Most of our electrical energy is generated by burning fossil fuels. New, gas-fired power stations are being opened and older coal-fired ones are being closed down. Describe the advantages and disadvantages of burning gas rather than coal.

....

....

....

....

....

.... (6)

3 The diagram illustrates some energy sources.

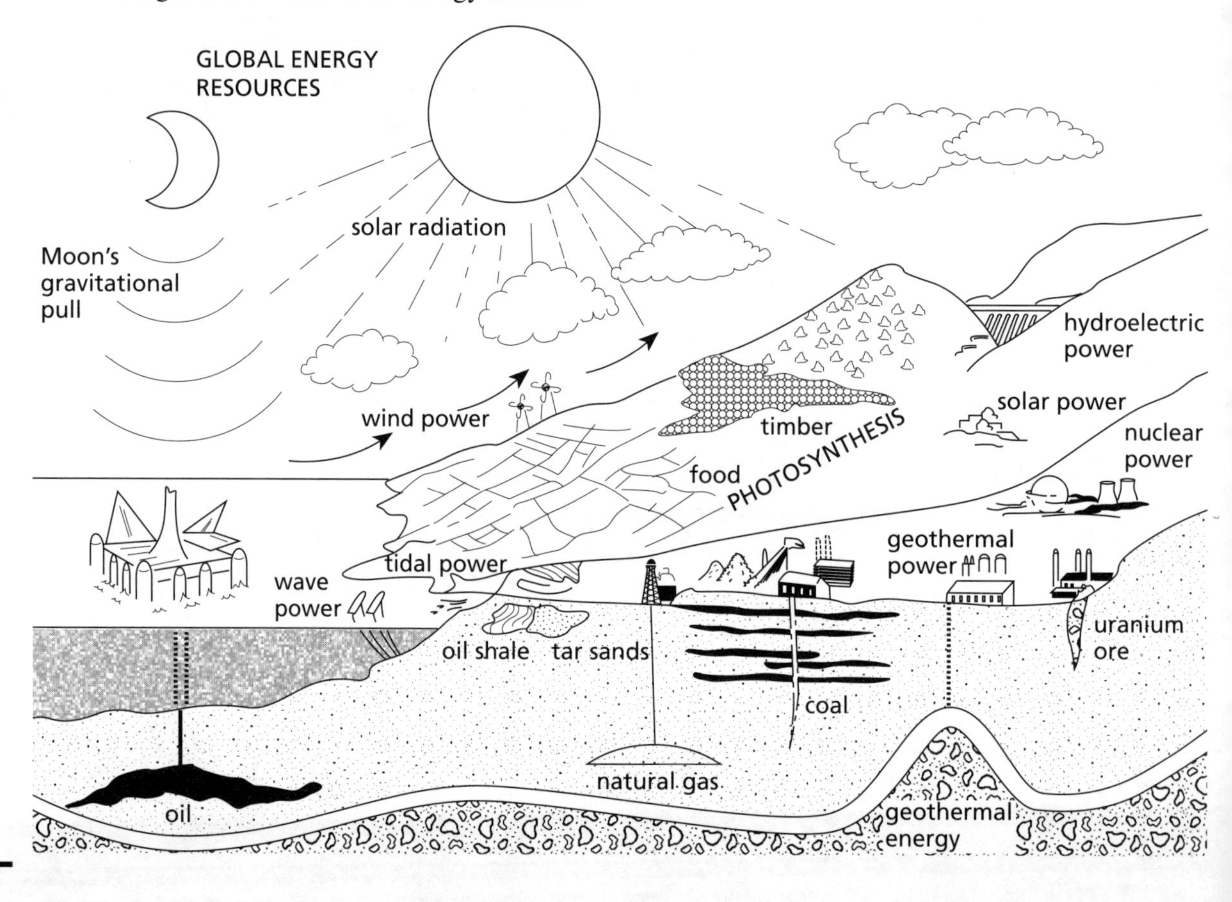

QUESTIONS

(a) (i) List **four** energy sources that are non-renewable.

....

....

.... (4)

(ii) List **four** energy sources that are renewable.

....

.... (4)

(iii) Which energy source stores energy from the Sun as gravitational potential energy?

.... (1)

(iv) Name **two** energy sources that store energy from the Sun as chemical energy.

.... (2)

(b) Solar power is unreliable in Britain but in some countries many houses use energy from the Sun to produce hot water for domestic use. The diagram shows how this can be done.

(i) Explain why the pipes are painted black.

.... (1)

(ii) State **two** reasons why copper pipes are used rather than iron pipes.

....

.... (2)

(iii) Explain why the pipes are contained in a glass-covered box.

....

.... (2)

(iv) Describe and explain how the water circulates in the system.

....

....

.... (3)

4 In some exposed parts of Britain the wind blows all the time. 'Wind farms' consisting of many wind turbines can produce as much electrical energy as a small coal-fired power station.

A typical wind turbine has an electrical power output of 3 MW (1 MW = 1×10^6 W).

(a) The power of the wind blowing through the turbine is 9 MW. Use the equation

efficiency = useful power output ÷ total power input

to calculate the efficiency of the turbine when the power output is 3 MW.

....

....

.... (2)

(b) One disadvantage of wind turbines is the high cost of manufacture and installation. State **three** advantages of wind turbines over a coal-fired power station.

....

....

.... (3)

(c) State **two** other disadvantages of using wind turbines to generate electricity.

....

.... (2)

QUESTIONS

5 Burning 1 litre of petrol releases 30 MJ of heat energy. The flow diagram shows what happens to this energy when 1 litre of petrol is burned in a car engine.

30 MJ from petrol

20 MJ wasted as heat in exhaust gases and cooling system

3 MJ wasted in mechanical system

7 MJ to drive car

(a) Use the definition of energy efficiency in question 4 to calculate the efficiency of the car engine.

....

.... (2)

(b) Describe what happens to the 20 MJ of energy which is wasted as heat in the exhaust gases and the cooling system.

.... (1)

(c) A car cooling system contains 6.3 litres of water. Each litre has a mass of 1.0 kg and the specific heat capacity of the water is 4200 J kg^{-1} °C^{-1}. On a cold day, the engine is started at a temperature of 5 °C and it reaches normal operating temperature at 95 °C. Calculate the energy absorbed by the water while the car is 'warming up'.

....

....

.... (3)

(d) The energy from burning fossil fuels in cars and other forms of transport ends up as thermal energy in the surroundings. Explain why it is not possible to use this energy to produce steam to drive a turbine and generate electricity.

....

....

.... (3)

QUESTIONS

(e) Heat pumps can use energy from the surroundings to heat buildings. A heat pump works like a refrigerator in reverse, extracting energy from the outside and transferring it to the inside of a building. The diagram represents a heat pump.

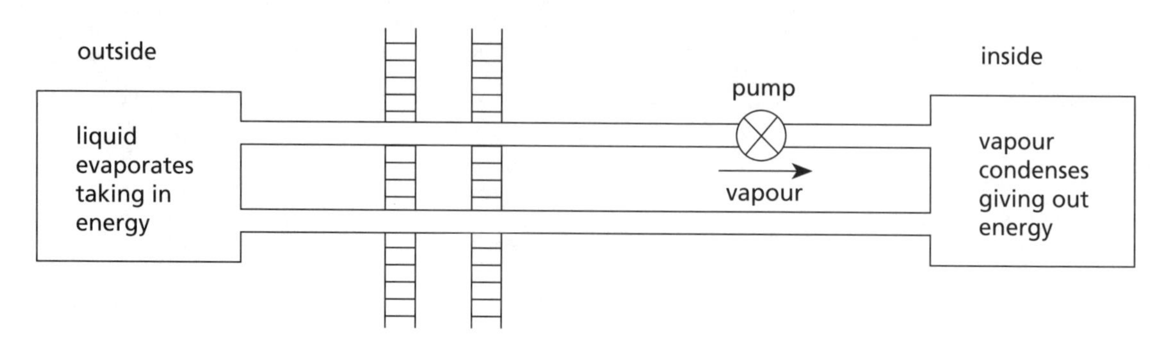

A 2.5 kW pump can transfer energy from the outside to the inside at a rate of 10 kW. Describe the advantages and disadvantages of using this method to heat a building.

....

....

.... (3)

The **pressure** caused by a force is a measure of how effective it is at piercing or deforming the surface that it acts on. Drawing pins and scissors are designed so that the force exerts a large pressure and penetrates the surface. Skis and caterpillar tracks on vehicles ensure that the force is applied over a large area to reduce the pressure. The formula for calculating pressure is:

$$\text{pressure} = \frac{\text{force}}{\text{area}} \qquad \text{or in symbols} \qquad p = \frac{F}{A}$$

The unit of pressure is the **pascal (Pa)** which is equivalent to a **N/m^2**.

In **hydraulic** systems, liquids are used to transmit pressure. Because liquids exert an equal pressure in all directions, the pressure can be easily transmitted round corners. By changing the **area** over which the pressure acts, the **force** can be made bigger or smaller.

Taps, bicycle pedals and doors are common examples of forces being used to turn things round. How effective a force is at causing rotation depends not only on the size of the force, but also the shortest distance from the line it acts along to the pivot. The **moment**, or **turning effect**, of a force is calculated using the formula:

$$\text{moment} = \text{force} \times \text{shortest (or perpendicular) distance from force line to pivot}$$

The moment, or turning effect, of a force is measured in **Nm**. In situations where the turning effects of a number of forces cancel out, the object is **balanced** or **in equilibrium**. This is known as the '**law of moments**' which states that: When an object is in equilibrium, the sum of the clockwise moments about any pivot is equal to the sum of the anticlockwise moments about that pivot.

Cars, bikes, buses, trains and other moving objects often have more than one force acting and so the overall effect of all the forces acting has to be taken into account. If the forces acting cancel out there is no effect on the movement of the object; it either stays put or moves in a straight line at a constant speed.

The **average speed** of a moving object is calculated using the equation:

$$\text{average speed} = \frac{\text{distance travelled}}{\text{time taken}} \qquad \text{or in symbols} \qquad v = \frac{d}{t}$$

When the forces are not balanced the effect is to change the speed or direction of an object. This is known as **acceleration** which is calculated using the formula

$$\text{acceleration} = \frac{\text{increase in velocity}}{\text{time taken}}$$

Acceleration can be thought of as the increase in speed per second and is measured in **m/s^2** or **$m\,s^{-2}$**.

The acceleration caused by an unbalanced force depends on the mass being accelerated as well as the size of the unbalanced force – a double decker bus needs a much bigger force than a mini car to give it the same acceleration. The equation which relates the mass of the object to the size of the unbalanced force and the acceleration it causes is:

$$\text{force} = \text{mass} \times \text{acceleration} \qquad \text{or in symbols} \qquad F = ma$$

Forces that cause movement are doing **work** and **transferring energy**. The amount of work done or energy transferred is calculated using the formula:

$$\text{work done} = \text{force} \times \text{distance moved in direction of force} \qquad \text{or in symbols} \qquad W = Fd$$

Work and energy are measured in **joules** (J).

REVISION SUMMARY

The rate at which work is done or energy is transferred is called the **power**; this is the work done by a force each second and is measured in **watts** (W). Power is calculated using the formula:

$$\text{power} = \frac{\text{work done/energy transfer}}{\text{time taken}} \quad \text{or in symbols} \quad P = \frac{E}{t}$$

Using a force to lift an object vertically is an example of transferring energy to **gravitational potential energy** (gpe for short). The gravitational potential energy gained by the object is calculated using the formula:

$$\text{change in gpe} = \text{weight} \times \text{change in height} \quad \text{or in symbols} \quad \text{gpe} = mg\Delta h$$

The symbol g stands for the gravitational field strength which is the weight of each kg of material. The gravitational field strength at the surface of the Earth is about $10\,\text{N}\,\text{kg}^{-1}$ and that at the surface of the Moon is about $1.5\,\text{N}\,\text{kg}^{-1}$.

When an object is changing speed its **kinetic energy** is changing. The formula for kinetic energy is:

$$\text{kinetic energy} = {}^1/_2 \times \text{mass} \times (\text{speed})^2 \quad \text{or in symbols} \quad \text{ke} = {}^1/_2 mv^2$$

Moving objects also have **momentum**; momentum is a useful concept when predicting the outcome of a collision or using information about the outcome of a collision to deduce what happened before the collision occurred. The momentum of an object is calculated using the formula:

$$\text{momentum} = \text{mass} \times \text{velocity} \quad \text{or in symbols} \quad p = mv$$

Momentum is measured in **N s** or **kg m s^{-1}**; the units are equivalent.

There are two important factors to remember about momentum; one is that the total amount of momentum of any system or group of objects stays the same and the second is that when adding the momentum of one object to that of another the direction has to be taken into account. The diagram illustrates this.

If you need to revise this subject more thoroughly, see the relevant topics in the Letts GCSE Physics Study Guide.

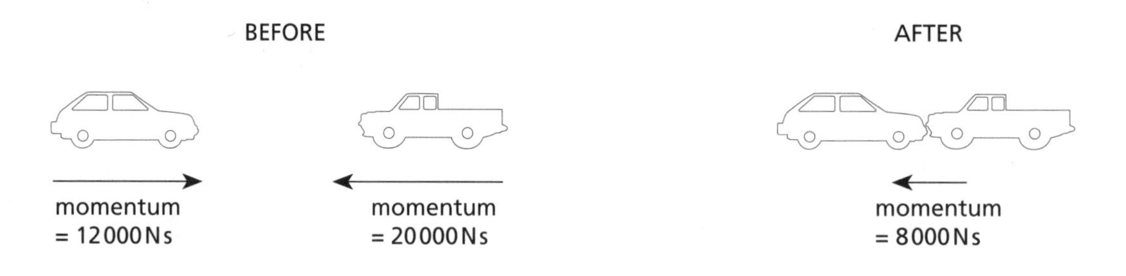

QUESTIONS

1 The arrows on the diagrams represent the horizontal forces acting on a car which is moving forwards. In each case the length of the arrow indicates the size of the force.

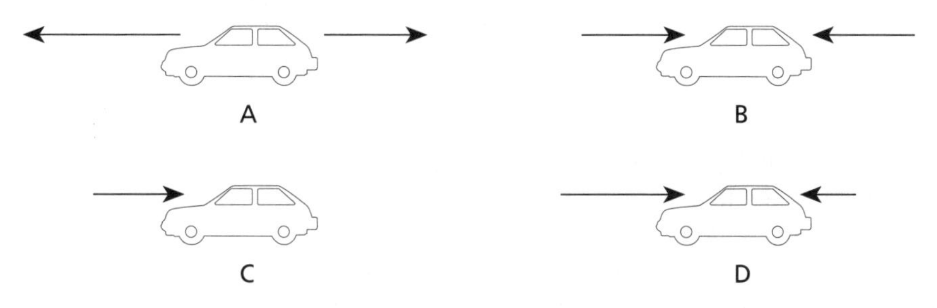

(a) Which diagram or diagrams could represent:

(i) a car that is accelerating? ....

(ii) a car that is slowing down? ....

(iii) a car travelling at a constant speed ? .... (4)

(b) (i) Calculate the average speed of a car that travels 240 m in 16 s.

....

.... (3)

(ii) Calculate the time it would take the car to travel at that average speed from Bristol to Hull, a distance of 330 km.

....

.... (3)

(c) (i) The size of the force that is pushing the car is 900 N. Calculate the work done by this force in pushing the car a distance of 240 m.

....

.... (3)

(ii) Calculate the power required to push the car for 240 m in 16 s.

....

.... (3)

QUESTIONS

2 (a)

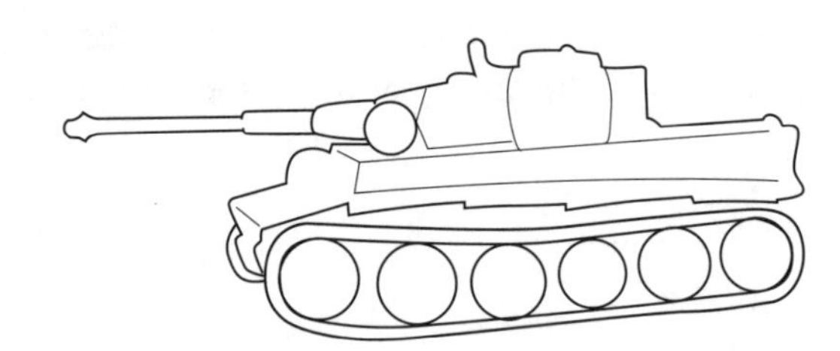

Tanks are very heavy. Without caterpillar tracks they would sink into soft ground. The tracks enable them to spread the weight over a large area, giving a small pressure on the ground underneath them.

The tank weighs 30 tonnes. This is the same as 300 000 N. The weight of the tank pushes down on the ground. The area of the tracks in contact with the ground is 20 m^2. Calculate the pressure on the ground.

....

....

.... (3)

(b) Nails have sharp points so that they can penetrate a material by exerting a large pressure. Explain how it is possible for a person to lie on a bed of nails without puncturing the skin.

....

.... (2)

3 The diagram shows the forces acting on a fishing rod when a fish has been 'hooked'.

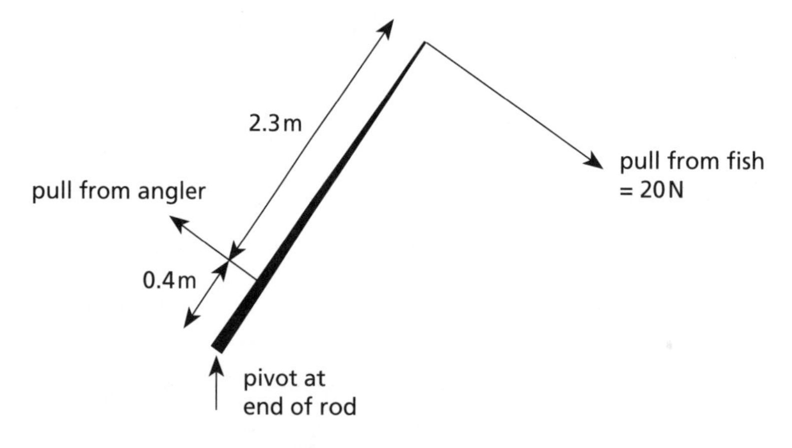

(a) Calculate the moment of the force from the fish.

....

....

.... (3)

(b) Calculate the force the angler must exert to stop the rod from turning clockwise.

....

....

.... (3)

(c) The angler using the rod has to exert a much bigger force than the fish does to maintain equilibrium. Explain what advantage the rod gives to the angler.

....

.... (2)

4 The diagram shows a tower crane.

counterbalance

load

(a) Explain why the crane would be unstable without the counterbalance.

....

.... (2)

(b) Explain why it is an advantage to have a counterbalance that can move towards or away from the tower.

....

.... (2)

(c) The crane in the diagram is lifting a load of 80 000 N (8 tonnes) which is 6 m from the tower. How far from the tower should a 100 000 N counterbalance be placed so that the crane is stable?

....

QUESTIONS

....

....

.... (3)

(d) The crane lifts the load through a vertical distance of 15.0 m. Calculate the amount of potential energy gained by the load.

....

....

.... (3)

(e) The speed at which the crane lifts the load is 0.3 m/s. Calculate the time it takes the crane to lift the load 15.0 m.

....

....

.... (3)

(f) Use your answers to (d) and (e) to calculate the power output of the crane in lifting the load.

....

....

.... (3)

5 (a) Calculate the momentum of each of the following:

(i) a 10 000 kg bus travelling at 15 m/s

.... (2)

(ii) a 100 g bullet travelling at 400 m/s

.... (1)

(iii) a 500 000 kg jumbo jet cruising at 300 m/s

.... (1)

(b) In foggy conditions on a motorway vehicles travelling in the same direction can collide.

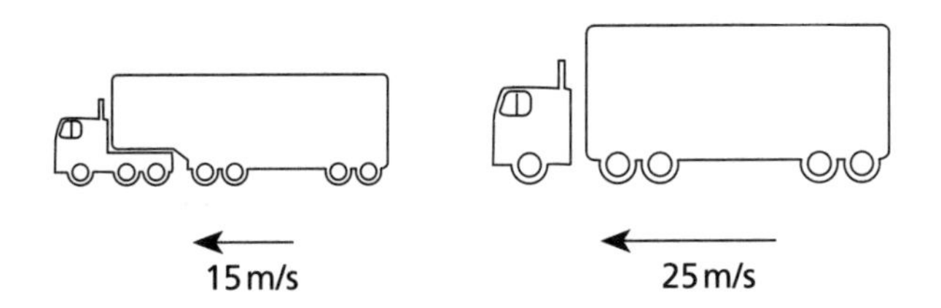

(i) Calculate the momentum of a 30 000 kg lorry travelling at 25 m/s and that of a 20 000 kg lorry travelling at 15 m/s.

....

....

.... (4)

(ii) The heavier lorry collides with the back of the lighter one and they stick together. Calculate the common speed immediately after the collision.

....

....

....

.... (4)

6 A Saturn V rocket fires its engines when it is outside the influence of any gravitational fields. It burns fuel at the rate of 13 000 kg per second. The exhaust gases have a speed of 2500 m/s.

(a) Calculate the change in momentum of the exhaust gases in one second.

....

....

.... (3)

(b) The rocket has a mass of 2.7×10^6 kg. Calculate the increase in speed of the rocket each second.

....

....

.... (3)

QUESTIONS

(c) The rocket continues to burn fuel at the same rate. Explain how the acceleration of the rocket changes as more fuel is burned.

....

....

.... (3)

7 A pedestrian steps into the path of an oncoming car. The graph shows how the speed of the car changes from the moment when the driver sees the pedestrian until the car stops.

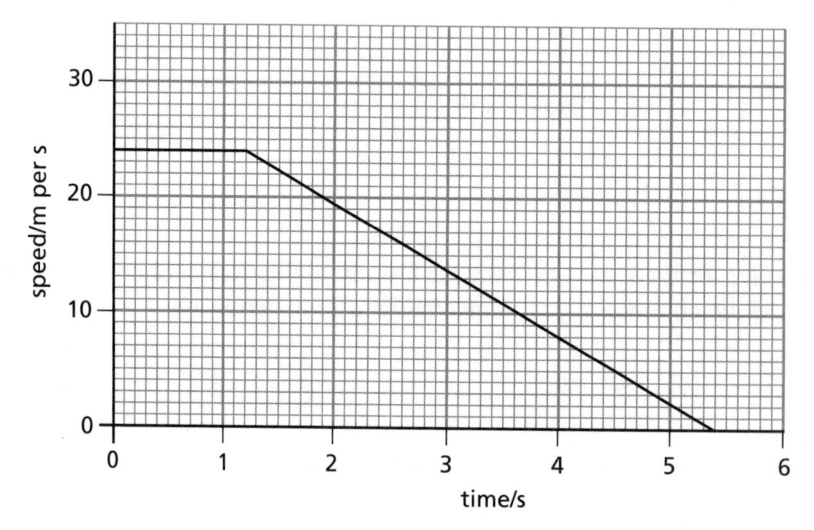

(a) (i) Explain why the first part of the graph shows the car continuing at constant speed.

....

.... (2)

(ii) How far does the car travel in the 1.2 s between the driver seeing the pedestrian and applying the brakes?

....

....

.... (3)

(iii) After 1.2 s the car slows down. Calculate the value of the deceleration of the car in this time.

....

....

.... (3)

(iv) Calculate the force which would be needed to cause a driver of mass 85 kg to have the same deceleration.

....

....

.... (3)

(b) The sequence of diagrams shows what can happen to the occupants of a car during a collision.

After the car has stopped, the driver continues to move forwards as the seat belt stretches.

(i) Explain why this stretching of the seat belt reduces the force which is exerted on the driver.

....

....

.... (3)

(ii) Explain why the child who was standing in the back of the car appears to have been thrown forwards.

....

....

.... (3)

(iii) Modern cars are designed to crumple when they are involved in a collision. Explain how this crumpling of the car helps to protect the occupants from serious injury.

....

....

.... (3)

MEG 1991

QUESTIONS

8 The diagram shows a simple hydraulic lifting device.

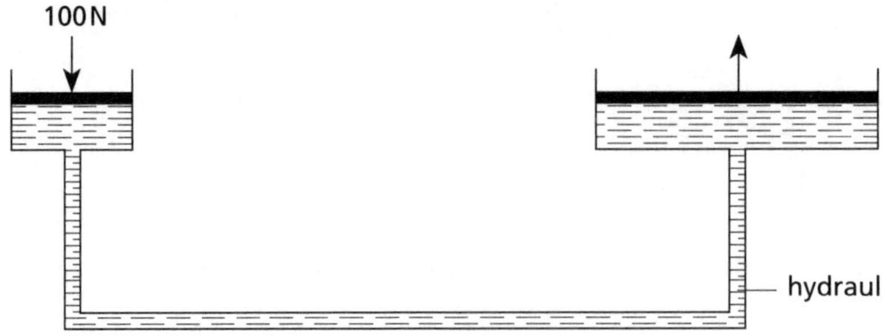

area of small platform = 5 cm^2

100 N

area of large platform = 25 cm^2

hydraulic fluid

(a) Calculate the pressure caused by the 100 N force.

....

....

....(3)

(b) What pressure is exerted by the fluid on the large platform?

....(1)

(c) Calculate the value of the upward force at the large platform.

....

....(2)

Sound is carried to our ears by a to-and-fro movement of air molecules. This to-and-fro movement starts with a **vibrating** object such as a loudspeaker which sets the air molecules into a **longitudinal** wave motion where the vibrations are along the direction in which the wave is travelling.

The maximum amount of displacement (movement to one side or the other) of the air molecules is called the **amplitude** of the wave; the greater the amplitude, the louder the sound. The graph shows how the movement of an individual air molecule changes with time.

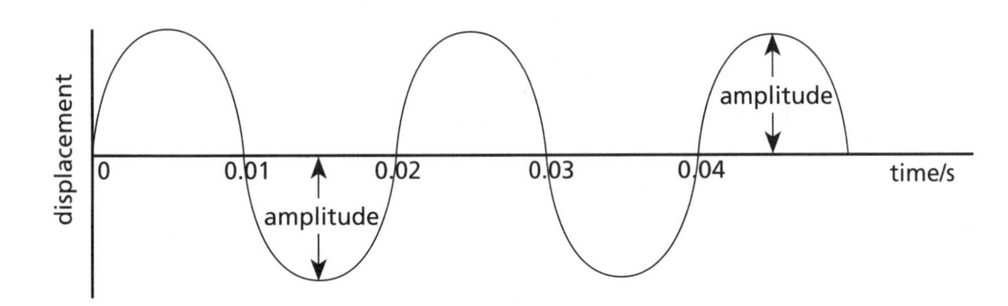

As well as showing the amplitude, the time scale on the graph enables the **frequency** to be measured. The frequency of a wave is the number of oscillations per second. The sound wave shown on the graph does one complete oscillation in 0.02 or 1/50 second so it has a frequency of 50 waves per second, or 50 hertz (Hz). The frequency of a sound wave determines its pitch; 50 Hz is quite a low-pitched sound but frequencies of 1000 Hz or more are high-pitched.

Measurements of the **wavelength** (the distance occupied by one complete cycle of the wave) and **frequency** allow the **speed** of sound to be calculated using the formula:

$$\text{speed} = \text{frequency} \times \text{wavelength} \quad \text{or in symbols} \quad v = f\lambda$$

Resonance is the name given to the build-up of large-amplitude vibrations when an object is forced to vibrate at a frequency which is equal to its natural frequency of vibration. Pushing a child on a swing is an example of resonance – the amplitude of the swing's vibration increases when the frequency of pushing coincides with the natural frequency of the swing, so that it receives a push once every complete oscillation. Resonance can be a nuisance when it leads to unwanted vibration such as in a washing machine or spin-drier. Electrical resonance is used to select which of the signals being received by the aerial a television or radio is tuned to.

Light is a small part of a family of waves called the **electromagnetic spectrum**. Most objects do not give off light so we rely on reflected light to be able to see them. All but the smoothest of surfaces reflect light in all directions. Mirrors are smooth surfaces that reflect light in a predictable way – the angles of incidence and reflection are equal. The reflection of light by a mirror causes a **virtual image** to be formed. Our eye-brain system assumes that light travels in straight lines so when we look into a mirror the reflected light looks to have come from a point the same distance behind the mirror as the object is in front of it.

Mirrors are not the only things that cause the direction in which light travels to change; light can also change direction when it passes through transparent objects such as glass. The change in speed when light passes from one substance to another is called **refraction**. This causes a change in wavelength and, except when light hits the boundary at a right angle, a change in direction. Although the wavelength and speed both change when light is refracted, the frequency, which determines the colour of the light, remains constant.

Light does not always pass into the new substance when it meets a boundary. Light travelling from glass to air is **totally internally reflected** for angles of incidence greater than 42°. Total internal reflection is used in bicycle reflectors, prism binoculars, cats' eyes and fibre optics.

REVISION SUMMARY

The table shows the main parts of the electromagnetic spectrum and their uses.

Wave	gamma rays	X-rays	ultra-violet	visible light	infra-red	microwaves	radio waves
Typical wavelength /m	1×10^{-12}	1×10^{-9}	1×10^{-7}	5×10^{-7}	1×10^{-6}	1×10^{-1}	100
Use	sterilizing medical equipment	X-ray photographs	treatment of skin disorders, responsible for suntans	seeing and transmitting data	heating and armchair operation of tv equipment	cooking and transmitting data	broadcasting

The shorter wavelength waves are the most penetrative and also the most ionizing so they pose the greatest dangers. Exposure to waves of shorter wavelength than light should be limited.

All electromagnetic waves are **transverse** waves – the vibrations are at right angles to the direction of travel. Radio waves from an aerial are **polarized**, which means that the vibrations are only in one plane. Light waves from a light source such as a lamp or the Sun are unpolarized. Light can be polarized by passing it through materials such as the Polaroid used in some sunglasses and light is partially polarized when it is reflected.

All waves spread out when they pass through a narrow opening; this is called **diffraction**. The amount of spreading depends on the size of the opening relative to the wavelength; if the opening is hundreds of wavelengths wide then very little spreading occurs, with maximum spreading when the opening is equal to the wavelength. Sound waves (typical wavelength 1 metre) spread out when passing through a doorway but light waves do not.

If you need to revise this subject more thoroughly, see the relevant topics in the Letts GCSE *Physics Study Guide*.

When two or more waves cross at any point they **interfere** with each other. When waves interfere they can combine to give an increase or decrease in disturbance at that point. If two wave crests or two wave troughs combine then constructive interference takes place but a wave crest and a trough combine to interfere destructively. Interference can be seen in surface water waves using a ripple tank; two dippers vibrating in step produce lines of constructive and destructive interference.

The separation of the lines of interference increases with increasing wavelength and distance from the sources but decreases when the sources are placed further apart. The interference of sound waves can be heard if two loudspeakers driven from the same signal generator are used as wave sources. Interference of light waves is more difficult to arrange using two sources but can be readily observed using a diffraction grating.

QUESTIONS

1 The diagram represents a loudspeaker cone. The circle represents an air molecule.

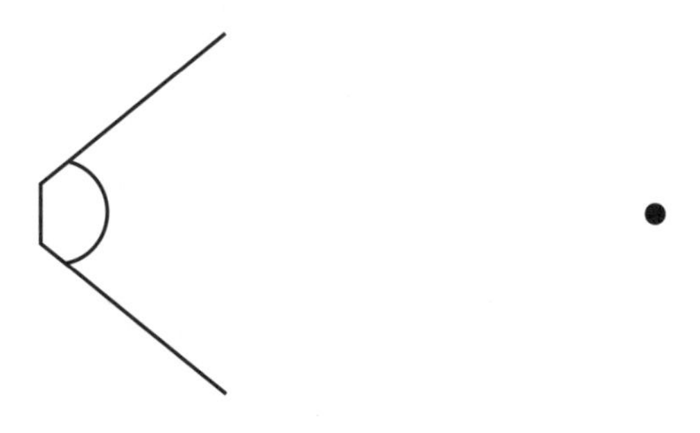

(a) (i) Describe the movement of the loudspeaker cone when the loudspeaker is producing sound of frequency 200 Hz.

....

.... (2)

(ii) Draw a series of sketch diagrams to show the movement of the air molecule as the sound wave passes.

....

....

....

.... (4)

(b) The graph shows how the displacement of the air molecule changes during one cycle of the wave.

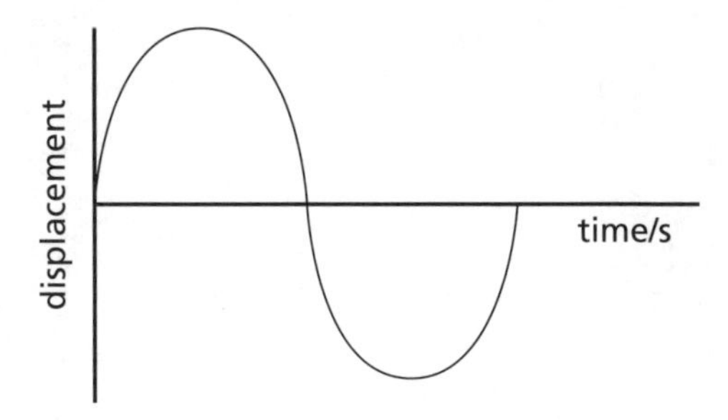

(i) Use the axes below to sketch a graph which shows the displacement of the air molecule when the volume of the sound is reduced with the frequency unaltered.

(2)

QUESTIONS

(ii) Use the axes below to sketch a graph which shows the displacement of the air molecule with the volume at its original level when the frequency is increased to 400 Hz.

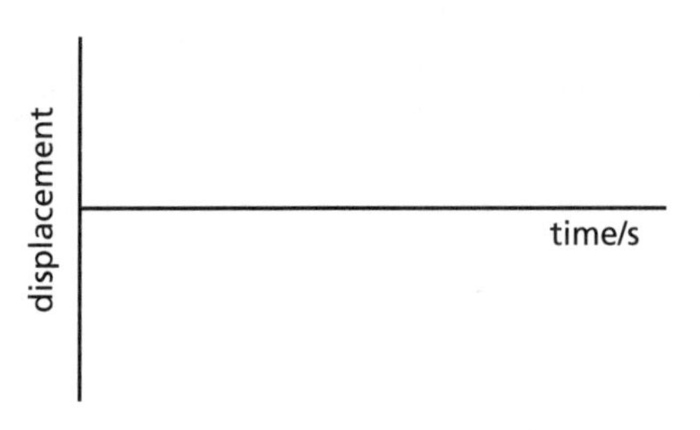

(2)

(c) Sound waves travel in air with a speed of 330 m/s. Calculate the wavelength of a sound wave which has a frequency of 200 Hz.

....

....

.... (3)

2 (a) When light passes through a window it slows down as it enters the glass and speeds up again when it leaves. The speed of light in glass is about two thirds of the speed of light in air. The diagrams show light waves about to travel through the glass. Complete the diagrams to show the passage of the light through the glass and out at the other side. (5)

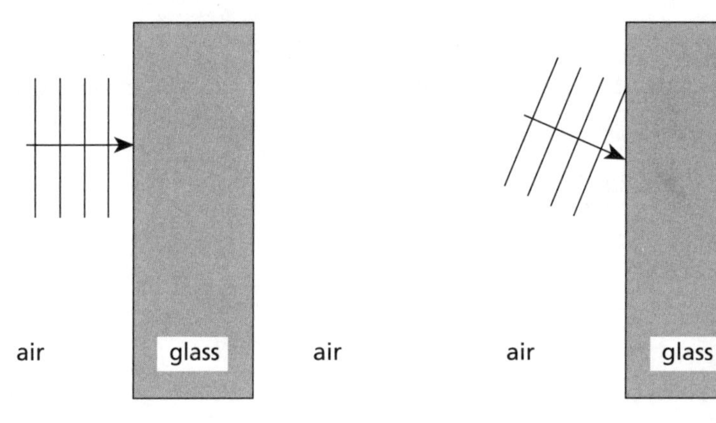

(b) Periscopes use either mirrors or prisms to turn light round corners. Complete the diagram of a periscope by continuing the light rays until they enter the eye. (4)

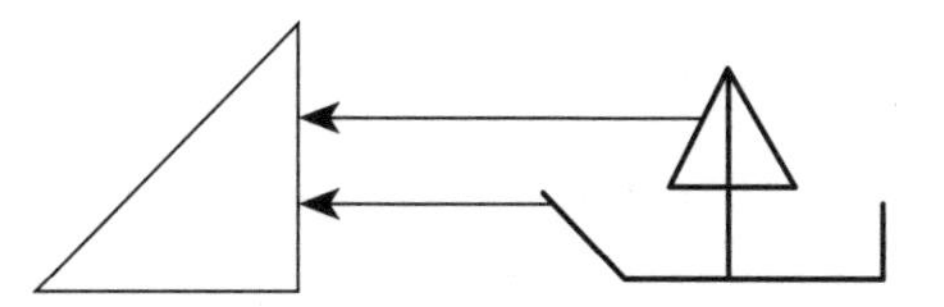

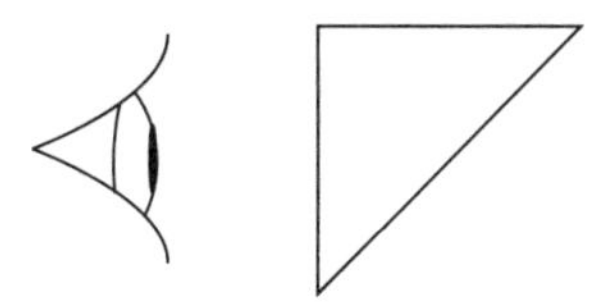

3 The diagram shows a transverse wave travelling along a rope.

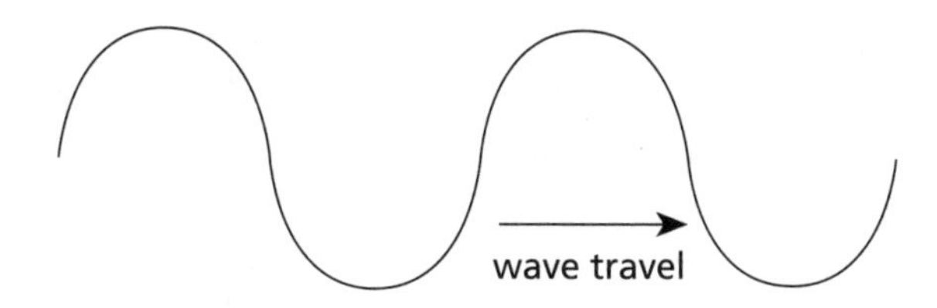

(a) (i) Describe the movement of each part of the rope as the wave travels along it.

....

....

....

.... (2)

(ii) Mark with an 'a' a distance which is equal to the amplitude of the wave. (1)

(iii) Mark with a 'λ' a distance which is equal to one wavelength of the wave. (1)

(iv) When the frequency of the wave is 1.5 Hz it has a wavelength of 7.5 m. Calculate the speed of the wave along the rope.

....

....

.... (3)

QUESTIONS

4 A person is sat in a room listening to music. The only lighting in the room is from a lamp in a ceiling fitting.

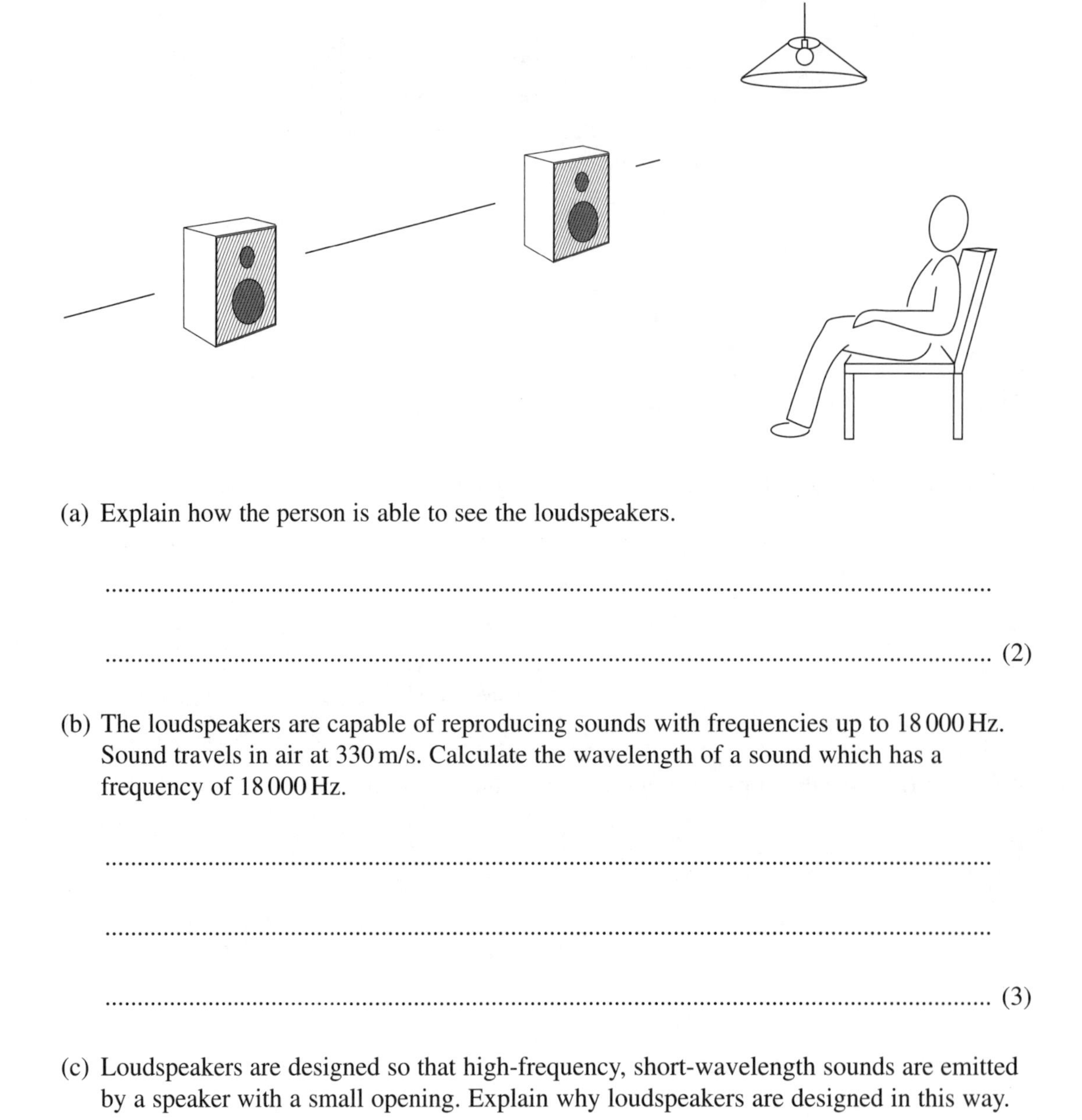

(a) Explain how the person is able to see the loudspeakers.

....

.... (2)

(b) The loudspeakers are capable of reproducing sounds with frequencies up to 18 000 Hz. Sound travels in air at 330 m/s. Calculate the wavelength of a sound which has a frequency of 18 000 Hz.

....

....

.... (3)

(c) Loudspeakers are designed so that high-frequency, short-wavelength sounds are emitted by a speaker with a small opening. Explain why loudspeakers are designed in this way.

....

....

.... (3)

(d) Resonance can be a nuisance in mechanical systems such as loudspeakers. Some inexpensive loudspeakers sometimes emit a 'grating' sound when a note of a particular frequency is played. Suggest what could cause this 'grating' sound to occur.

....

....

.... (3)

(e) The diagram represents a person standing outside the room.

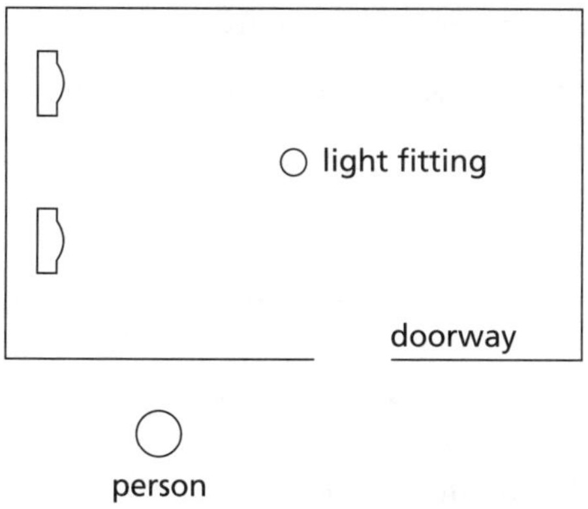

light fitting
doorway
person

The sound from the loudspeakers reaches the person through the open doorway but the light does not.

(i) Use a diagram to explain how the sound reaches the person outside the room.

(3)

(ii) Explain why the light from the lamp does not reach the person outside the room.

....

....

.... (3)

5 Microwave cookers heat food using radio waves of wavelength 0.12 m. The speed of the waves is $3.0 \times 10^8 \mathrm{m\,s^{-1}}$.

QUESTIONS

(a) Calculate the frequency of the waves used in microwave cooking.

....

....

.... (3)

(b) The microwaves cause water molecules in food to resonate.

(i) Describe what happens when the water molecules resonate.

....

....

.... (3)

(ii) Explain how this causes the food to become hot.

....

.... (2)

(iii) Pyrex dishes and other food containers are not heated by the microwaves. What does this tell you about the frequency at which the molecules in Pyrex oscillate?

....

.... (1)

6 The diagram shows two radio transmitters. The transmitters are broadcasting identical radio waves of wavelength 3.0 m.

A person walks between the transmitters, listening to the broadcast on a walkman. He notices that the sound gets louder, then quieter, then louder and so on as he walks. When he stands still the loudness of the sound stays the same, but there are some places where the sound is loud and other places where it is quiet.

QUESTIONS

(a) Use diagrams to explain how the radio waves from the transmitters combine to give a very strong radio signal at some points and a weak signal at others. (4)

(b) Suggest why this could be a nuisance to a householder who lives within the range of both transmitters.

....

.... (2)

(c) Interference of radio wave from adjacent transmitters can be overcome if one transmitter emits waves that are horizontally polarized and the other uses vertical polarization.
Explain the meaning of polarization of radio waves, and describe the difference between horizontal polarization and vertical polarization.

....

....

....

.... (3)

5 The Earth's place in the Universe

REVISION SUMMARY

The **Universe** is thought to have begun in an enormous explosion about fifteen billion years ago. The name 'Universe' means everything – stars, planets, asteroids, galaxies and everything that exists. Within the Universe there are groups of stars called **galaxies**. Our star is the Sun and our galaxy is the **Milky Way**, which is a whirling spiral, held together by the attractive **gravitational forces** that act between massive objects.

Gravitational forces act between all objects that have mass but they are only significant when one of the objects is very massive. There is, for example, a gravitational force between two pencils placed one centimetre apart on a desktop but it is a tiny force and is not big enough to overcome the frictional forces that resist motion. Gravitational attraction between the planets and the Sun keep the planets in **orbit** around the Sun. The orbits are actually **ellipses** but they are almost circular.

All circular motion requires an **unbalanced force** acting towards the centre of the circle. Without the gravitational pull, the planets would not stay in orbit around the Sun. Imagine whirling a rubber bung tied to a piece of string; you have to keep pulling on the string to keep the bung going round in a circle.

Gravitational forces act between objects, with each object pulling the other. While the Earth's pull on the Moon keeps the Moon in orbit around the Earth, the most obvious effect of the Moon's pull on the Earth is in causing the movement of water that creates **tides**.

Although the Earth has only one natural satellite, there are many artificial ones. Like the **Moon**, they are kept in orbit by the gravitational attraction of the Earth. This gravitational attraction decreases with increasing distance from the Earth. Low-orbit satellites go round the Earth in one and a half hours but communications satellites are usually placed further from the Earth where the orbit time is twenty four hours; in this way they stay above the same point on the Earth's surface.

The Sun is the energy source for the Earth and the rest of the Solar System. This energy comes from the **fusion** reaction taking place in the Sun. Our Sun, like the other stars in the Universe, probably started life as a cloud of hydrogen. Gravitational forces caused the cloud to contract and become hot, reaching a temperature of millions of degrees. At these temperatures hydrogen nuclei join together to form helium nuclei, a reaction which releases a large amount of energy.

Our Sun is not as old as the Universe. The Solar System is thought to have been formed from material ejected by an exploding star. The core of this cloud of material formed the Sun, with the outermost material condensing to form the planets. In addition to the nine planets, there is the **asteroid** belt and, on the far reaches of the Solar System, collections of ice and dust known as **comets**. The comets have very long orbit times, often hundreds of years.

The inner planets, Mercury, Venus, Earth and Mars, are the denser ones in the Solar System; they have a high concentration of metals. Jupiter and Saturn are composed largely of hydrogen and helium. Jupiter has many moons, one of which, Io, is the most geologically active body in the Solar System. Less is known about the composition of the three outermost planets. Uranus and Neptune are thought to be composed mainly of hydrogen and helium, but Pluto is thought to consist mainly of ice and rock.

The Universe is still expanding, as it has been doing since its formation. When the paths of the galaxies are plotted, all these paths trace back to the same point. This is thought to be the point where the Universe was created. The age of the Universe is estimated by measuring the speed at which the galaxies are moving away from each other and extrapolating back to the beginning of time.

There are three possibilities for the future of the Universe. It may carry on expanding for ever or the gravitational forces may slow down the expansion and eventually cause it to contract again with catastrophic results. The third model is that the gravitational forces are not strong enough to cause a collapse but are just strong enough to prevent continued expansion, so the Universe will eventually reach a stable size.

If you need to revise this subject more thoroughly, see the relevant topics in the *Letts GCSE Physics Study Guide*.

QUESTIONS

1 The table gives some information about each of the three innermost planets.

planet	atmosphere	surface	surface temperature / °C	density/g cm^{-3}
Mercury	very little	dry and heavily cratered	varies between −200 and 400	5.4
Venus	carbon dioxide with sulphuric acid clouds	dry with some craters	constant at 450	5.3
Earth	mainly oxygen and nitrogen with water vapour clouds	mixed water and dry with very few craters	some variation around an average of 15	5.5

(a) Mercury, like the Earth's moon, is heavily cratered. These craters are thought to be almost as old as the Solar System itself.

(i) Suggest how these craters could have been formed.

....

.... (2)

(ii) Venus and the Earth have very few craters. Much of the Earth's surface is covered in water and it is thought that Venus once had a watery surface. Both of these planets have atmospheres. Use this information to suggest why Venus and Earth have very few craters.

....

....

....

....

.... (4)

(b) The surface temperature of a planet is determined by two factors; its distance from the Sun and the greenhouse effect.

(i) Mercury rotates on its axis comparatively slowly: one Mercury day lasts for 58 Earth days. Explain why the temperature on Mercury's surface varies between very hot and very cold.

....

....

.... (2)

QUESTIONS

(ii) Although Venus is further from the Sun than Mercury is, its surface temperature is hotter than that of Mercury and it shows very little variation. Suggest **two** reasons for this.

....

....

.... (2)

(iii) Although Venus receives approximately twice as much radiant energy from the Sun as the Earth does, very little of this reaches the surface of Venus. Much of it is reflected or absorbed by its atmosphere. Suggest why the surface of Venus is very much hotter than that of Earth.

....

....

.... (2)

(c) The innermost planets are the dense planets. Mercury, Venus and Earth all have similar densities. What does this suggest about the chemical make-up of Mercury and Venus?

....

.... (1)

2 Much of the Earth's surface is covered in water. The diagram shows how the gravitational field of the Moon causes the water to bulge.

Moon

X

Earth

(a) Mark the positions of the high and low tides with the letters 'H' and 'L'. (4)

(b) Describe how the water level at X would change over a 24-hour period due to the Earth's rotation in the direction shown in the diagram.

....

....

.... (3)

(c) As a result of the movement of the Moon around the Earth, the time interval between successive high tides is approximately $12\frac{1}{2}$ hours. Draw a line on the diagram to show the path of the Moon in a 24-hour period. (2)

3 Comets, like the planets, go round the Sun in elliptical orbits. The orbit times of comets range from a few years to millions of years. The diagram shows a comet orbit.

Sun

(a) Describe and explain how the speed of a comet changes as it approaches the Sun.

....

.... (2)

(b) Mark an 's' on the diagram at the point where you would expect the comet to have its smallest speed. (1)

(c) Comets have a structure similar to that of the moons of the outer planets, mainly ice. Comets become visible as a glow when their distance from the Sun is approximately three times the radius of the Earth's orbit.

(i) Suggest what is happening to a glowing comet to make it visible.

....

....

.... (2)

(ii) Describe how you would expect the mass of a comet to change as it completes one complete orbit around the Sun.

....

.... (2)

(d) Comets leave trails of dust in their wake as they pass close to the Sun. Bright lights can be seen in the Earth's atmosphere when the Earth passes through these dust clouds. Suggest what happens to cause these bright lights.

....

.... (2)

6 Atomic and molecular Physics

REVISION SUMMARY

The **kinetic theory** uses our understanding of the behaviour of individual **atoms** and **molecules** to explain the properties of materials made up of large numbers of atoms and molecules. Important evidence that molecules are constantly moving comes from the observation of larger particles suspended in air or water. Smoke specks in air and carbon specks in water can be seen to move in an erratic, jerky motion. This movement is called **Brownian motion** after Robert Brown, the person who is credited with first observing it. The explanation for Brownian motion is due to Einstein who argued that the specks must be subjected to bombardment and since the bombarding particles are much smaller than the specks, they must be moving at very high speeds.

This gives a picture of **gas** molecules as being in constant, rapid, unordered motion, making frequent collisions with other molecules and the walls of the containing vessel. The density of gases suggests that the average spacing between gas molecules is approximately ten molecular diameters. **Liquids** are denser than gases and are pictured as being more close-packed with less freedom of movement; their motion can be described as 'jostling'. **Solids** have a fixed shape due to the molecules being in fixed positions but the molecules in a solid are not 'still'. Their motion is a constant vibration at high frequency.

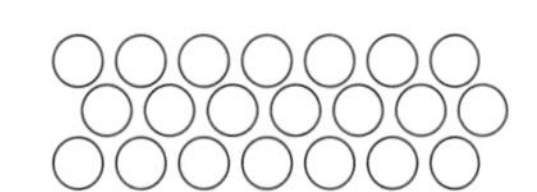

the molecules in a crystalline solid are in a regular array

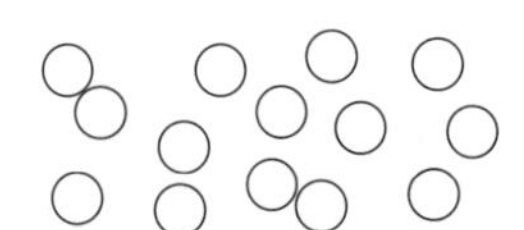

the molecules in a liquid are constantly colliding

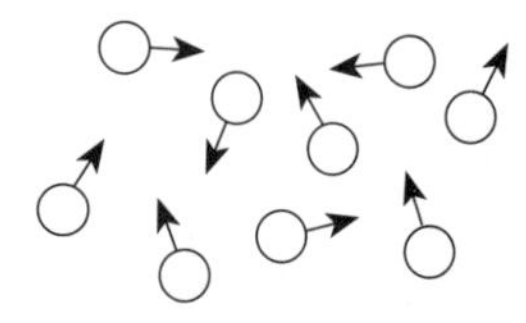

gas molecules move freely

Temperature is a measure of the energy of the molecular movement; the higher the temperature, the more energy the molecules have.

Whilst a gas expands to fill the space available, solids and liquids keep a fixed volume due to the attractive forces between the molecules. The molecules in a liquid are, on average, slightly further apart than those in a solid. Energy is needed to **melt** a solid because work has to be done to increase the molecular separation. Similarly, energy is needed to **vaporize** a liquid. Boiling water doesn't suddenly change to steam, a lot of energy is needed to do this. More energy is needed to vaporize a liquid than to melt the same quantity of solid because vaporization involves a much greater increase in molecular separation. When substances **condense** or **solidify**, energy is released as the molecular separation decreases.

Diffusion is the name given to the process where substances mix together when placed in contact. Diffusion in gases is a rapid process – cooking smells travel quickly – but diffusion in liquids and solids is much slower because the molecules only travel short distances between collisions.

Unlike solids and liquids, gases are squashy because of the large spacing between molecules. Most of the volume occupied by a gas at room temperature is free space, and the molecules can be pushed into this space. Gases exert pressure by colliding with the container walls.

When a gas is squashed into half its original volume, the molecular concentration is doubled, resulting in twice the rate of collisions with the container walls and twice the pressure. The gas pressure is also affected by temperature; increasing the temperature makes the collisions more frequent because the molecules have a greater average speed. Experiment shows that doubling the kelvin temperature of a gas doubles the pressure it exerts if other factors are kept constant. Changes in pressure, temperature and volume are summarized by the gas equation which describes what happens when a gas changes from state 1 to state 2:

$$\frac{\text{pressure}_1 \times \text{volume}_1}{\text{temperature}_1} = \frac{\text{pressure}_2 \times \text{volume}_2}{\text{temperature}_2} \quad \text{or in symbols} \quad \frac{p_1V_1}{T_1} = \frac{p_2V_2}{T_2}$$

Radioctive decay occurs when an unstable nucleus emits energy in the form of electromagnetic radiation or a particle when it changes to a more stable nucleus. The following table summarizes the three types of radiation that can be emitted.

REVISION SUMMARY

type of nuclear radiation	nature	charge	penetration	ionizing ability
alpha	two neutrons and two protons, sometimes referred to as a helium nucleus	positive	stopped by a few cm of air or a thin piece of card	intensely ionizing
beta	high-speed electron emitted when a neutron decays to a proton and an electron	negative	partially absorbed by aluminium foil; totally absorbed by 5 mm aluminium	less than alpha; ionization occurs at collisions with atoms and molecules
gamma	high-frequency, short-wavelength electromagnetic radiation	none	never totally absorbed; intensity is reduced by thick lead or concrete	weakly ionizing; the high penetration is due to few collisions where ionization would occur

Many elements exist in different forms called **isotopes**, some of which are more stable than others. The different isotopes of an element have the same electron arrangement and the same number of protons but differ in the number of neutrons. The most common form of carbon is carbon-12 (the 12 refers to the total number of protons and electrons) but the isotope carbon-14, an unstable form of carbon, also exists in nature. The table compares the isotopes.

isotope	electron arrangement	number of protons	number of neutrons
carbon-12	2, 4	6	6
carbon-14	2, 4	6	8

When carbon-14 decays it emits a beta particle as a neutron becomes a proton and the atom changes to a nitrogen atom.

$$^{14}_{6}C \rightarrow {}^{14}_{7}N + e^{-}$$

Note that in the symbolic equation the top number to the left of the atomic symbol represents the **mass number**, or total number of protons and neutrons, and the bottom number is the **atomic number**, or number of protons.

Carbon-14 decays with a **half-life** of 5730 years. This means that half of the carbon-14 atoms in a sample of carbon change to nitrogen during this time. After one half-life of a material half of the unstable atoms are still present and the rate of decay has halved. These numbers halve again to a quarter of the original value after a second half-life and so on.

All living things contain a constant proportion of carbon-14; when they die they stop taking in new supplies of carbon-14 and so the proportion goes down as the carbon-14 decays. The time since the death of plant or animal material can be estimated by measuring the proportion of carbon-14 present and calculating the number of half-lives that have elapsed since death. This is a technique known as **radio-carbon dating**.

Radioactive isotopes are widely used in medicine for detecting and treating illness, for killing bacteria and for tracing the movement of fluids.

Nuclear power relies on the energy released when a large, unstable nucleus is split, or 'fissioned', into smaller ones. The splitting of the nucleus is triggered when a neutron is absorbed. As well as energy, other neutrons are released which can go on to cause more fissions.

In a nuclear reactor a coolant is used to extract the thermal energy released as a result of the fission process. Fission is kept at a constant rate by control rods which absorb the extra neutrons; if all the neutrons produced were allowed to cause further fissions then the reaction would quickly get out of control. Another important feature of a reactor is the moderator; this slows down the neutrons released so that they can be captured by other uranium nuclei.

If you need to revise this subject more thoroughly, see the relevant topics in the Letts GCSE *Physics Study Guide*.

QUESTIONS

1 (a) Smoke particles in air can be observed using a low power microscope. They move in an erratic way. The diagram shows the path of a smoke particle in air.

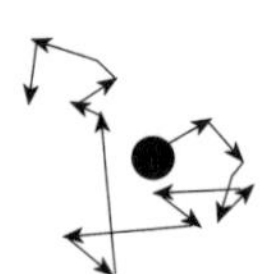

(i) Describe the motion of the smoke particle.

....

.... (2)

(ii) Explain how the movement of the smoke particle provides evidence about the motion of air molecules.

....

....

....

.... (4)

(b) A crystal of a bright red dye is placed at the bottom of a beaker of still water.

dye crystal

(i) On the right hand diagram, sketch what you would expect to see a few days later. (2)

(ii) Explain, in terms of moving molecules, how this change has taken place. A sketch could help to make your answer clear.

....

....

.... (3)

QUESTIONS

2 In a diesel engine, air is drawn into a cylinder and then squashed rapidly. This causes the temperature to rise.

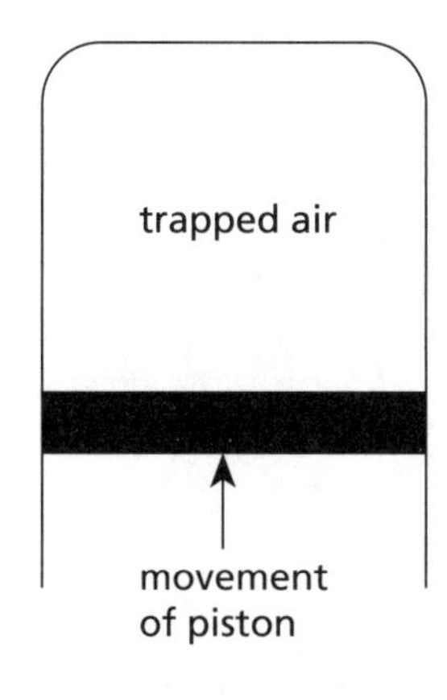

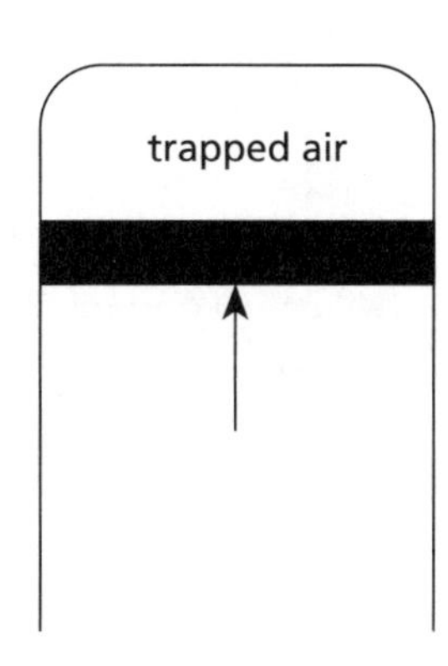

(a) Explain why the pressure of the trapped air increases.

....

....

....

.... (4)

(b) Use the data in the table to calculate the pressure of the air compressed by the moving piston.

	air before compression	air after compression
pressure/kPa	100	
volume/cm^3	400	25
temperature/K	290	700

....

....

....

.... (4)

3 The diagram shows the main components of a smoke detector.

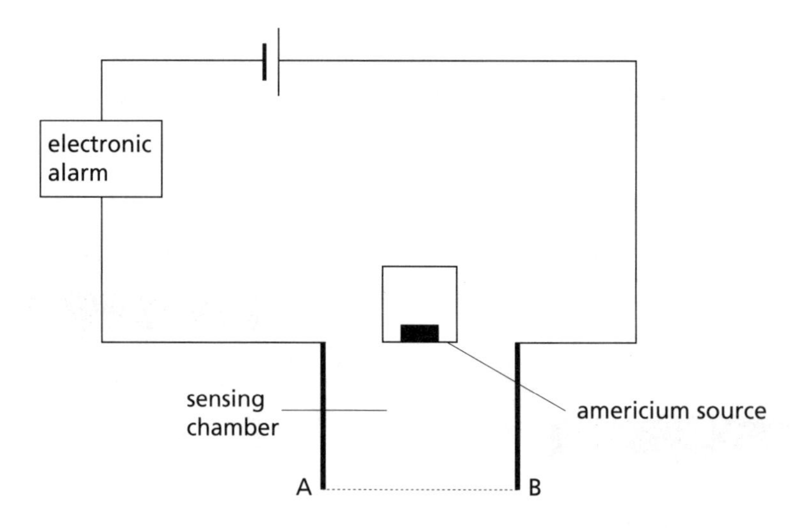

The detector uses a very weak source of americium. This gives off alpha particles which collide with air molecules in the sensing chamber. As a result of the collisions, the air molecules become ionized and a current passes between the electrodes A and B. When smoke enters the sensing chamber the ionization current is reduced and this causes the alarm to sound.

(a) Explain why the radiation from the americium source is not dangerous to the people living in the house.

....

.... (2)

(b) Describe what happens to the air molecules when they become ionized, and explain how this enables a current to pass between the electrodes.

....

....

.... (3)

(c) Would the alarm work just as well if the americium were to be replaced with a beta source of the same strength? Explain your answer fully.

....

.... (2)

(d) Use the graph below to find the half-life of the americium source.

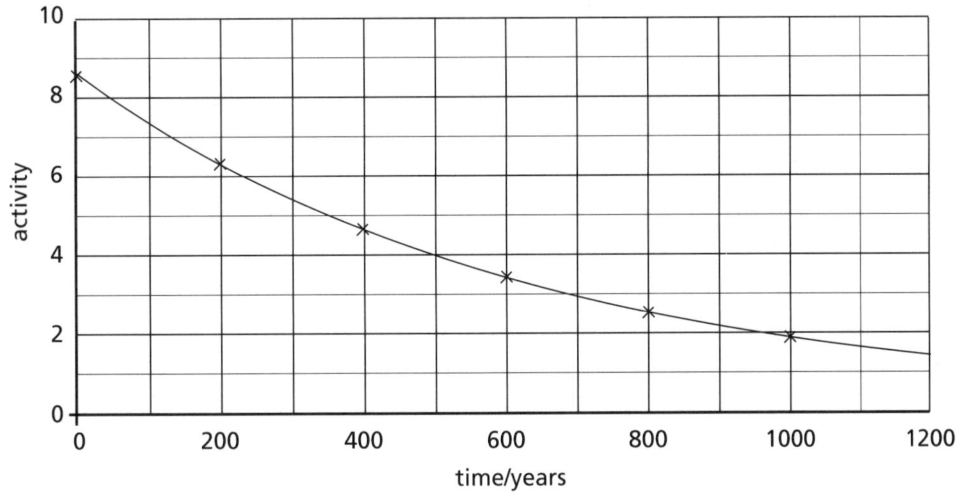

Half-life of americium = ... (2)

ULEAC 1991

4 Radioactive materials are used in hospitals as tracers. The isotope commonly used is technetium-99. This is attached to another chemical so that it is directed to the organ being investigated. The radioactive tracer is injected into the patient's bloodstream and after a short time a photograph is taken to show its distribution in the body. Technetium-99 emits gamma radiation.

(a) Explain why gamma is a suitable radiation to use for this purpose.

....

.... (2)

(b) Describe the dangers to a patient if an alpha- or beta-emitter were used instead.

....

....

.... (3)

QUESTIONS

(c) When choosing a radioactive material for a particular purpose, the half-life has to be considered.

(i) Describe the meaning of the term half-life.

....

.... (2)

(ii) Technetium-99 has a half-life of 6 hours. Suggest why this is a suitable half-life for tracers used in medicine.

....

.... (2)

Physics and the atmosphere

REVISION SUMMARY

The composition of the Earth's atmosphere today is very different to its composition before there was life. As early plant life **photosynthesized**, a **carbon dioxide-rich** atmosphere was converted into an **oxygen-rich** one. It is important for life on Earth that the current composition of the atmosphere, shown in the table, is maintained.

substance	approximate percentage by volume
nitrogen	78
oxygen	21
argon	1
carbon dioxide	0.03
water vapour	varies between 0 and 5

All the substances shown in the table are continually being **recycled** by the Earth. The **water cycle** relies on energy from the Sun evaporating water from the seas and oceans. The water vapour rises and condenses into clouds as it cools. This is followed by **precipitation** when the purified water returns to Earth as rain, hail or snow.

The rate at which water evaporates from the seas and oceans depends on the temperatures of the air and the water. Warm air can absorb more water vapour than cold air and warm water evaporates at a greater rate than cold water. The prevailing wind in this country is from the west; air streams reaching the west coast have just travelled across the Atlantic Ocean. When the wind blows from the north it brings unusually cold weather and a wind from the south can bring a heat-wave. **Winds** are caused by differences in pressure in the Earth's atmosphere. These arise from a combination of the Earth's spin, convection currents and differential heating.

Convection currents can be both local and global. In coastal regions sea breezes occur during the daytime in summer due to the land warming faster than the sea. The breezes change direction in the evening as the land cools rapidly, making the sea warmer. Global convection currents are due to two factors; radiant energy from the Sun is spread over a smaller area at the equator than the poles and that reaching the equator has also travelled through less atmosphere. The atmosphere absorbs and scatters some of the Sun's radiation, so the more atmosphere the radiation has travelled through, the less of it reaches the Earth.

Convection currents are also responsible for **cloud** formation. Most of the Sun's radiant energy is absorbed by the ground,which then heats the air in contact with it. This warm air rises and cools until it reaches a temperature at which water vapour condenses into tiny water droplets. Further cooling, which could be caused by an air stream rising as it crosses a hill or mountain, causes the drops to become larger and fall as rain.

Cold, **frosty** nights are associated with little or no cloud cover. The temperature drops rapidly, causing the water vapour in the air to condense and then freeze. If the air is very moist, the condensing vapour may form a **fog**. On a clear night, the infra-red radiation emitted by the Earth goes straight into space and very little comes back to us. On a cloudy night, this infra-red radiation is absorbed by the clouds and some of it is radiated back to the Earth, reducing the amount by which the Earth cools down.

The **fronts** that are seen on weather maps are places where moving masses of air at different temperatures meet together. A **warm front** occurs when warm air moves towards colder air. Because the warm air is less dense, it rises above the colder air mass. At a **cold front** the cold air is moving into a region occupied by warmer air, which again results in the warm air being pushed upwards. Rain is likely to occur at both warm and cold fronts as the rising warm air cools and water vapour condenses.

If you need to revise this subject more thoroughly, see the relevant topics in the *Letts GCSE Physics Study Guide*.

QUESTIONS

1 The diagram illustrates the water cycle.

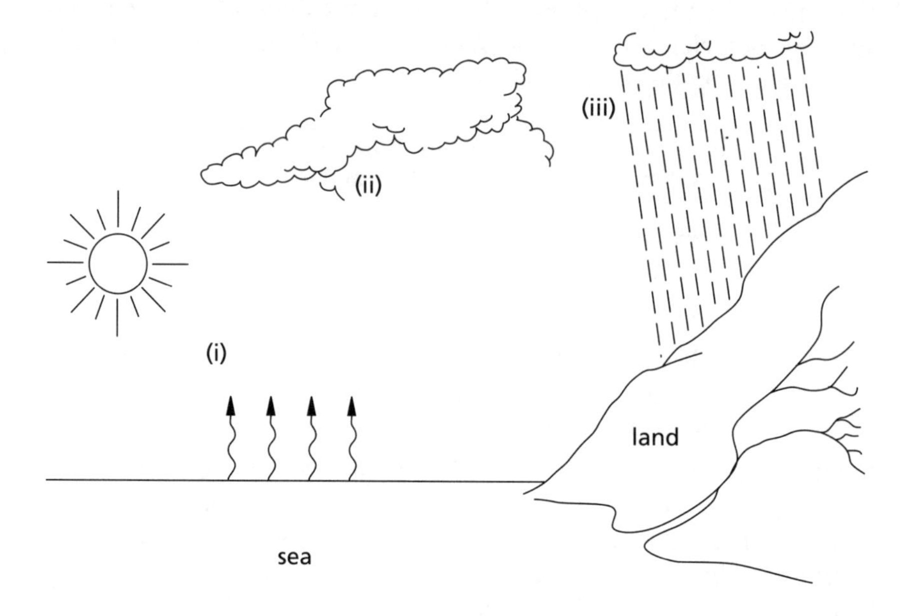

(a) Explain what is happening at the points labelled (i), (ii) and (iii).

(i) ....

....

....

(ii) ....

....

....

(iii) ....

....

.... (9)

(b) Name the source of energy for the water cycle.

.... (1)

2 Hail stones are formed by moving air masses within a cloud.

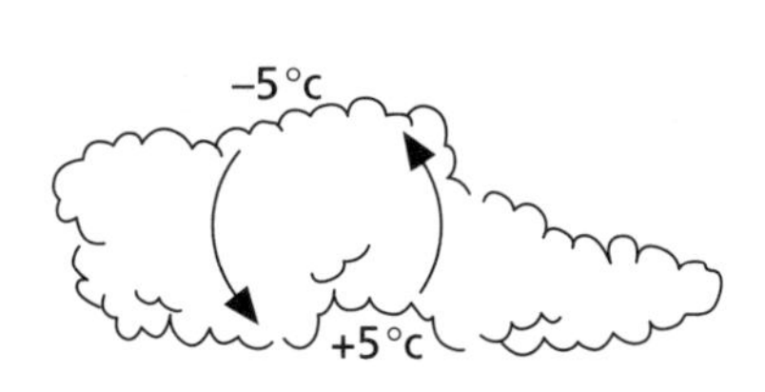

(a) Describe how the base of the cloud is warmed.

....

....

.... (3)

(b) Explain why water drops freeze as they are driven upwards in the cloud.

....

.... (2)

(c) The frozen water drops become larger and heavier as they move down in the cloud. Suggest what causes this.

....

.... (2)

(d) Before a hailstone falls to Earth, it has travelled up and down in the cloud several times. Suggest why hail stones have a layered structure.

....

.... (2)

QUESTIONS

3 The diagram shows the carbon dioxide cycle.

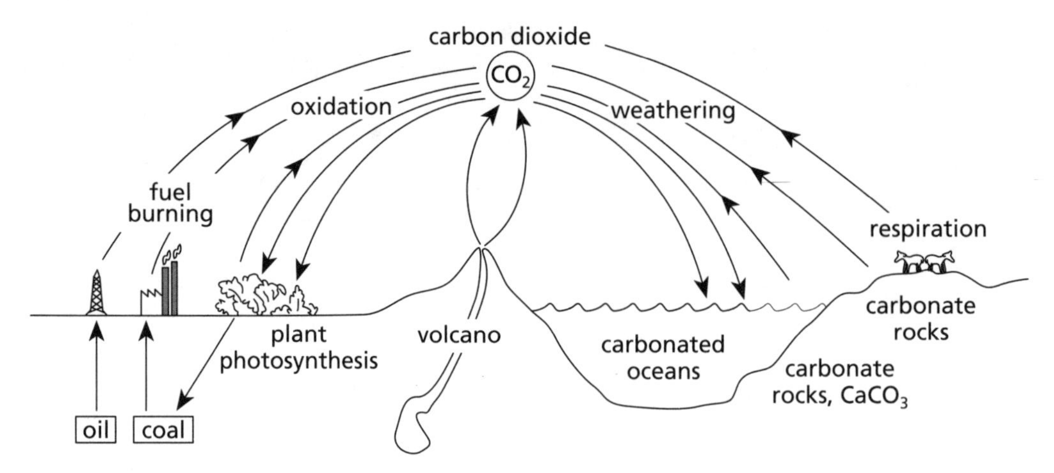

(a) Which of the processes shown in the diagram increase the amount of carbon dioxide in the atmosphere?

....

....

....

.... (5)

(b) Which of the processes decrease the amount of carbon dioxide in the atmosphere?

....

.... (2)

(c) The Earth's atmosphere may have been formed from volcanic eruptions. The main gases present in volcanic eruptions are water, carbon dioxide, sulphur dioxide and nitrogen.
Early life on Earth consisted of water-based plants such as algae. Suggest how these plants could have changed the composition of the atmosphere.

....

....

.... (3)

(d) Explain how the balance of carbon dioxide in the atmosphere is dependent on both plant and animal life.

....

.... (2)

1 ELECTRICITY AND MAGNETISM

Question			Answer	Mark
1	(a)	(i)	OR 0 AND 0	1
		(ii)	OR 1 AND 1	1
		(iii)	OR 1 AND 0	1
		(iv)	OR 1 AND 0	1

Examiner's tip Unless stated otherwise, an OR gate has a '1' output when either or both of the inputs are '1'.

		Answer	Mark
	(b)	Line i	1
	(c)	Lines iii and iv	1
	(d)	Either door A or door B has to be opened.	1
		And the master switch has to be on.	1

Examiner's tip The condition that either door A or door B has to be opened includes the possibility of both being opened at once.

		Answer	Mark
	(e)	The latch keeps the alarm switched on.	1
		After a door has been closed.	1

		Answer	Mark
2	(a)	B is the best conductor.	1
		Because it needs the smallest potential difference to cause the same current.	1
	(b)	Knowledge that $R = V \div I$	1
		$= 0.6\,\text{V} \div 0.8\,\text{A}$	1
		$= 0.75\,\Omega$	1

Examiner's tip You must have the correct unit for the third mark; if your answer is 0.75 with no unit or the wrong unit you gain two marks out of the three. Although you would usually gain full marks for the correct answer with no working, showing your working allows you to gain some credit, e.g. for knowledge of the formula, even if your final answer is wrong.

		Answer	Mark
	(c)	Knowledge of the formula $P = I \times V$	1
		The power in wire A $P = 0.8\,\text{A} \times 5.2\,\text{V}$	1
		$= 4.16\,\text{W}$	1
		Similarly for wire B, $P = 0.48\,\text{W}$ and for C, $P = 9.92\,\text{W}$	1
		C gets hottest because it has the greatest power.	1

Examiner's tip When you are asked to 'explain why', you must give a reason. The reason in this case is 'because it has the greatest power'.

		Answer	Mark
	(d)	Knowledge of the formula $Q = It$	1

Question	Answer	Mark
	For each wire $Q = 0.8\,\text{A} \times 60\,\text{s}$	1
	$= 48\,\text{C}$	1

Examiner's tip As the wires carry the same current, the same quantity of charge flows through each in one minute. For the formula to be valid, the current must be in amps and the time in seconds.

Question	Answer	Mark
3 (a)	and	1
	or	1

Examiner's tip Circuit 1 is called a series circuit and circuit 2 is a parallel circuit.

Question	Answer	Mark
(b)	In circuit A the variable resistor enables the brightness of the lamp to be changed.	1
	In circuit B the variable resistor enables the speed of the motor to be changed.	1
(c)	There are two possible ways of doing this. The switch and a battery or power supply should be in series with each other (1mark); the lamp and the motor can be either in series or in parallel (1 mark). The third mark is for having the correct circuit symbols. The diagrams show the two possible solutions.	3

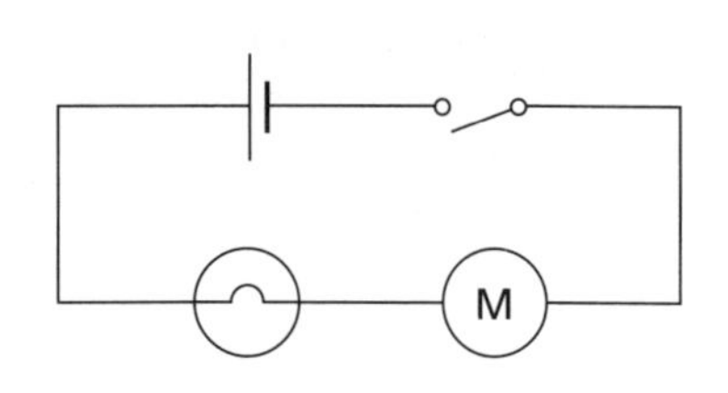

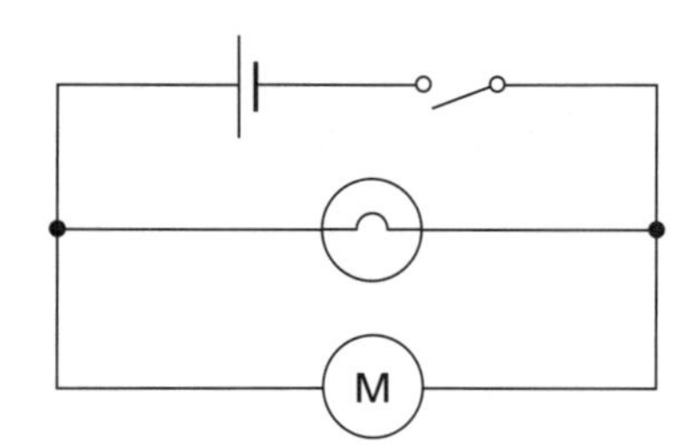

Examiner's tip The blobs show that there is an electrical connection where the wires cross. When drawing circuit diagrams, take care not to leave gaps when drawing a connecting wire to a component such as a lamp.

Question	Answer	Mark
(d)	The variable resistor should be in series with the motor.	1
	The lamp should be in parallel with the motor and variable resistor.	1
	The battery or power supply forms the third parallel branch of the circuit.	1

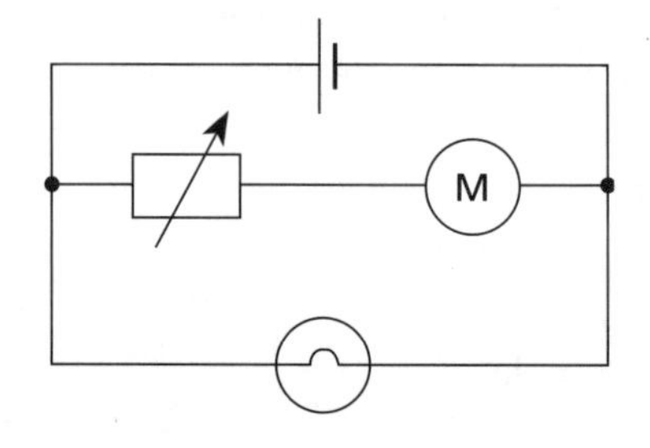

Question	Answer	Mark
4 (a)	The compass needles should be pointing in a clockwise circle; one mark for each two correct.	2
(b)	Wrap the wire into a coil of several turns.	1
	Use an iron core in the centre of this coil.	1

Examiner's tip 'Increase the current/voltage' would also be acceptable answers but 'Use a bigger power pack/battery' would not, since 'bigger' refers to the physical size.

Question	Answer	Mark
(c)	The coil of wire has a magnetic field.	1
	This magnetizes the iron core.	1
	The L-shaped iron is attracted to the iron core.	1
	Which causes the switch contacts to be pressed together.	1
(d)	The completed circuit is	

	One mark for having a complete circuit with the correct symbols.	1
	One mark for having the switch contacts, power supply and lamp in series.	1

Question	Answer	Mark
5 (a)	There is a changing magnetic field in and around the coil.	1
	This induces a voltage which causes a current in the coil.	1

Examiner's tip When answering questions about electromagnetic induction, it is important to emphasize whether or not the magnetic field is changing.

Question	Answer	Mark
(b) (i)	There is no reading on the ammeter.	1
	Because the magnetic field around the coil is not changing.	1
(ii)	The ammeter deflection is to the left.	1
	Because the change of field has been reversed.	1

Examiner's tip Note that reversing the magnet or the direction of movement causes the current to pass in the opposite direction.

Question	Answer	Mark
(iii)	The current alternates, changing direction when the movement of the magnet changes direction.	1
	The current is bigger than before because the movement is faster, so the magnetic field changes at a greater rate.	1

Question			Answer	Mark
6	(a)		The ratio of the voltages is 1:16	**1**
			The turns ratio is the same, so the number is $16 \times 20\,000 = 320\,000$	**1**
	(b)		**Either** to reduce the current transmitted	
			or to reduce the power losses	**1**
7	(a)		The sliding contact should be at the left-hand side.	**1**
			So that the variable resistor does not contribute any resistance to the circuit.	**1**
			This gives the least total resistance and the maximum current.	**1**
	(b)		Knowledge of the formula $I = P \div V$	**1**
			$= 1000\,\text{W} \div 240\,\text{V}$	**1**
			$= 4.17\,\text{A}$	**1**
8	(a)		When the circuit is switched on the heater outputs thermal energy.	**1**
			This causes the temperature of the sensor to increase.	**1**
			Which in turn causes the heater to turn off.	**1**
	(b)		The current in the heater is too great for the transistor switch to handle.	**1**
			The relay enables the large current in the heater to be switched by a much smaller current.	**1**
	(c)	(i)	$9 - 0.6 = 8.4\,\text{V}$	**1**

Examiner's tip Note that in a series circuit the total potential difference is the sum of the potential differences across the components.

Question			Answer	Mark
		(ii)	Knowledge of the formula $I = V \div R$	**1**
			Circuit current $= 8.4\,\text{V} \div 1000\,\Omega$	**1**
			$= 0.0084\,\text{A}$ or $8.4\,\text{mA}$	**1**
			Thermistor resistance $= 0.6\,\text{V} \div 0.0084\,\text{A}$	
			$= 71.4\,\Omega$	**1**

Examiner's tip This assumes that the amount of current that passes into the transistor switch is so small it can be neglected, so that the current in the fixed resistor and the thermistor is the same.

Question			Answer	Mark
		(iii)	The current in the thermistor has a heating effect.	**1**
			This needs to be minimized so that it does not turn the heater off even though the temperature is too low.	**1**
	(d)		The 9 V potential difference in the sensing circuit is shared between the thermistor and the fixed resistor.	**1**
			When the thermistor gets warmer its resistance drops and its share of the p.d. goes down.	**1**
			The transistor switch is turned off when the p.d. across the thermistor drops below 0.6 V.	**1**

Question	Answer	Mark

Examiner's tip In a series circuit of two resistors, the potential difference is shared in the same ratio as the resistances. This means that if there is a change in the resistance of one of the resistors, the potential difference across both of them changes.

2 ENERGY RESOURCES AND ENERGY TRANSFER

Question		Answer		Mark
1	(a)	A man pushing a supermarket trolley	✓	1
		A girl pedalling a bicycle	✓	1
		A shelf supporting some books		1
		A gas flame heating some water	✓	1
		The weight of a building pushing down on the ground		1
		Water evaporating from the sea	✓	1
		The upward push of the sea on a floating ship		1
		The upward push on a rising hot-air balloon	✓	1
	(b)	A coffee maker is designed to transfer electrical energy		1
		into thermal (or heat) energy.		1
		A television set is designed to transfer electrical energy		1
		into light energy (or radiant energy)		1
		and sound energy.		1
		A bunsen burner is designed to transfer chemical energy		1
		into thermal (or heat) energy.		1
	(c)	19 J		1
		of thermal (heat) energy.		1

Examiner's tip This is an example of the principle of conservation of energy, which states that energy cannot be created or destroyed; it can only change from one form into others. This means that the total energy going into a device must equal the total energy that comes out.

Question			Answer	Mark
2	(a)	(i)	The water at X is heated by a convection current.	1
			The water next to the heater becomes hot and less dense.	1
			This warmer, less dense water rises.	1

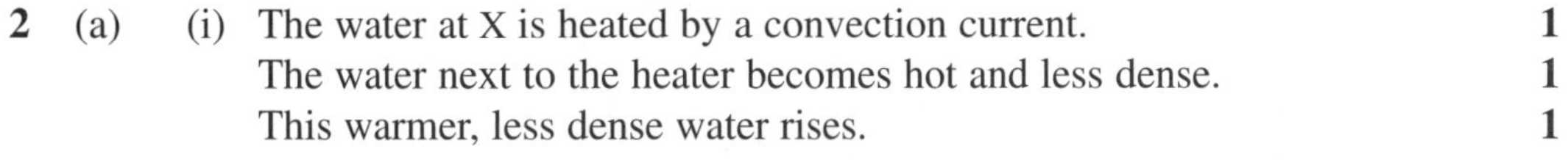

Examiner's tip You should avoid using the phrase 'heat rises' – it is not true. In a convection current, the hot or cold fluid moves due to a difference in densities.

Question			Answer	Mark
		(ii)	The energy travels by conduction.	1
			Energy is passed from molecule to molecule.	1
			It is a slow process because water is a poor conductor of thermal energy.	1

Question	Answer	Mark

Examiner's tip You should appreciate that non-metals are poor conductors of electrical energy and thermal energy.

(b)	(i)	The energy absorbed = mass × shc × temperature rise	1
		= 200 kg × 4200 J kg^{-1} °C^{-1} × 40 °C	1
		= 33.6 MJ or 3.36×10^7 J	1

Examiner's tip Note that the first mark is for knowledge of the formula. You gain all three marks if you have the correct answer and unit.

	(ii)	Energy is also needed to heat the tank.	1
		And energy is lost to the cooler surroundings.	1
(c)		Burning gas does not produce ash.	1
		Burning gas does not produce smoke.	1
		Gas is easier to transport; once the pipeline is built it does not need access to a road or rail network.	1
		Reserves of gas are much less than those of coal.	1
		Redundancies in coal mines need to be considered.	1
		As does the effect of higher unemployment/loss of mining communities.	1

Examiner's tip In answering a question like this one, your answers should come under the headings of social, environmental and economic issues.

3	(a)	(i)	Any four from gas, oil, coal, tar, uranium, geothermal.	**4** (1 mark each)
		(ii)	Any four from wind, wave, hydroelectric, tides, timber, food.	**4** (1 mark each)

Examiner's tip Although vegetation such as timber is renewable, coal is not. This is because the timescale over which coal is formed from rotting vegetation is millions of years.

	(iii)	Hydroelectric power stores energy from the Sun as gravitational potential energy of water.	1
	(iv)	Any two from food, timber, coal, oil, gas, tar.	**2** (1 mark each)
(b)	(i)	Black is the best absorber of radiant energy.	1
	(ii)	Copper is a better conductor of thermal energy.	1
		Copper does not corrode.	1
	(iii)	The box acts like a greenhouse.	1
		It reduces the amount of energy lost by radiation.	1

Examiner's tip An alternative answer would be that the glass covering allows radiant energy to enter but does not allow air to enter and cool the pipes.

Question			Answer	Mark
		(iv)	Water is heated in the pipes and rises.	1
			This happens because it is less dense than the colder water.	1
			Cold, denser water from the bottom of the tank moves down to replace it.	1
4	(a)		Efficiency = 3 MW ÷ 9 MW	1
			= 0.33	1

Examiner's tip Efficiency is expressed as a number less than 1 or as a percentage. It does not have a unit.

Question		Answer	Mark
	(b)	Wind turbines have low running costs.	1
		They do not use fossil reserves.	1
		They do not cause atmospheric pollution.	1
	(c)	Wind turbines occupy a lot of room.	1
		They are noisy/do not work if there is no wind.	1
5	(a)	Efficiency = 7 MJ ÷ 30 MJ	1
		= 0.23	1
	(b)	The energy warms up the surrounding air.	1

Examiner's tip All the energy from burning the petrol eventually ends up as unrecoverable thermal energy in the surroundings.

Question		Answer	Mark
	(c)	Energy absorbed = mass × shc × temperature rise	1
		$= 6.3\,\text{kg} \times 4200\,\text{J kg}^{-1}\,°\text{C}^{-1} \times 90\,°\text{C}$	1
		$= 2.38\,\text{MJ}$ or $2.38 \times 10^6\,\text{J}$	1
	(d)	The energy is spread out into a large mass.	1
		Causing a small temperature rise.	1
		Temperatures in excess of 100°C are needed to generate steam.	1
	(e)	The cost of the energy used to drive the pump is relatively low.	1
		Fossil fuel consumption is reduced.	1
		The least amount of energy is available when it is most needed, when the outside temperature is cold.	1

3 FORCES AND THEIR EFFECTS

Question			Answer	Mark
1	(a)	(i)	Diagram A shows a car that is accelerating forwards.	1
		(ii)	Diagrams C and D show cars that are travelling forwards and slowing down.	2
		(iii)	Diagram B shows a car travelling at a constant speed.	1

Question		Answer	Mark
(b)	(i)	Knowledge of formula speed = distance ÷ time	1
		= 240 m ÷ 16 s	1
		= 15 m/s	1

Examiner's tip Note that the correct answer and unit gains full marks, but always show your working in case you make an arithmetical mistake; this allows you to be awarded partial credit even though your final answer may be wrong. You gain two marks if you have the correct answer but wrong or missing unit.

Question		Answer	Mark
	(ii)	Rearrangement of formula to give time = distance ÷ speed	1
		= 330 000 m ÷ 15 m/s	1
		= 22 000 s	1
(c)	(i)	Knowledge of formula work = force × distance moved	1
		= 900 N × 240 m	1
		= 216 000 J	1
	(ii)	Knowledge of formula power = work done ÷ time taken	1
		= 216 000 J ÷ 16 s	1
		= 13 500 W	1

Examiner's tip If you made a mistake in (c)(i) that should not affect your marks in (ii) since an examiner will work through with your wrong answer. For example, if your answer to (i) was 900 N ÷ 240 m = 3.75 J then this would be marked wrong but an answer to (ii) based on this, i.e. 3.75 J ÷ 16 s = 0.23 W would then be marked correct.

Question	Answer	Mark
2 (a)	Knowledge of formula pressure = force ÷ area	1
	= 300 000 N ÷ 20 m^2	1
	= 15 000 Pa (N/m^2)	1
(b)	The area of a number of nails is larger than that of one nail.	1
	This gives a smaller pressure than just one nail.	1

Examiner's tip Some students confuse the words 'force' and 'pressure'. It is correct to write that 'the force is spread over a large area, giving a small pressure' but 'the pressure is spread out' is wrong.

Question	Answer	Mark
3 (a)	Knowledge of formula	
	moment = force × (perpendicular) distance to pivot	1
	= 20 N × 2.7 m	1
	= 54.0 N m	1
(b)	For equilibrium the moment of the angler's force must also equal 54 N m	1
	force = moment ÷ distance to pivot = 54 N m ÷ 0.4 m	1
	= 135 N	1

Question	Answer	Mark
(c)	The rod acts as a distance magnifier.	1
	This enables a small movement from the angler to move the fish a larger distance.	1
4 (a)	The load has a turning effect on the crane.	1
	This would cause the crane to topple (rotate clockwise).	1
(b)	Moving the counterbalance changes its moment.	1
	This allows for different loads to be lifted or the load to be moved towards or further away from the tower.	1
(c)	The moment of the load = 80 000 N × 6 m = 480 000 N m	1
	The counterbalance must have an equal but opposite moment	1
	Distance of counterbalance = 480 000 N m ÷ 100 000 N = 4.8 m	1
(d)	Knowledge of formula gpe = weight × change in height	1
	= 80 000 N × 15 m	1
	= 1 200 000 J	1
(e)	Knowledge of formula time = distance ÷ speed	1
	= 15.0 m ÷ 0.3 m/s	1
	= 50 s	1
(f)	Knowledge of formula power = work done ÷ time taken	1
	= 1 200 000 J ÷ 50 s	1
	= 24 000 W	1
5 (a) (i)	Knowledge of formula momentum = mass × velocity	1
	momentum = 10 000 kg × 15 m/s = 150 000 N s	1
(ii)	momentum = 0.1 kg × 400 m/s = 40 N s	1

Examiner's tip Always use kg, m and s when calculating physical quantities.

Question	Answer	Mark
(iii)	momentum = 500 000 kg × 300 m/s = 150 000 000 N s	1
(b) (i)	momentum of 30 000 kg lorry = 30 000 kg × 25 m/s	1
	= 750 000 Ns	1
	momentum of 20 000 kg lorry = 20 000 kg × 15 m/s	1
	= 300 000 N s	1
(ii)	Total momentum after the collision = 1 050 000 N s	1
	Combined mass of lorries = 50 000 kg	1
	New speed = 1 050 000 N s ÷ 50 000 kg	1
	= 21 m/s	1

Examiner's tip This relies on the principle of conservation of momentum; when two objects collide, the total momentum after the collision is equal to the total momentum before the collision.

Question	Answer	Mark
6 (a)	Knowledge of formula momentum = mass × velocity	1
	= 13 000 kg × 2 500 m/s	1
	= 32 500 000 Ns	1
(b)	The rocket gains 32 500 000 N s of momentum each second	1
	increase in speed = $3.25 \times 10^7 \div 2.7 \times 10^6$ kg	1
	= 12.0 m/s	1

Examiner's tip Rocket engines work on the principle that when the hot exhaust gases gain momentum in a 'backwards' direction, this causes the rocket to have an equal momentum change in the 'forwards' direction.

Question	Answer	Mark
(c)	The total mass of the rocket decreases as it burns fuel.	1
	The propelling force (or rate of change of momentum) remains the same.	1
	So the acceleration increases.	1
7 (a) (i)	There is a delay before the driver reacts (reaction time).	1
	This time elapses before the driver brakes.	1
(ii)	Knowledge of formula distance = speed × time	1
	= 24 m/s × 1.2 s	1
	= 28.8 m	1
(iii)	Knowledge of formula deceleration = decrease in speed ÷ time	1
	= 24 m/s ÷ 4.2 s	1
	= 5.7 m s^{-2}	1
(iv)	Knowledge of formula force = mass × acceleration	1
	= 85 kg × 5.7 m s^{-2}	1
	= 485 N	1
(b) (i)	The stretching of the seatbelt increases the time it takes to halt the driver.	1
	This reduces the deceleration of the driver.	1
	So a smaller force is exerted on the driver.	1
(ii)	The child carries on moving when the car has stopped.	1
	At the speed of the car before the collision.	1
	Because there is no force to decelerate her.	1

Examiner's tip In answering this question, students often write that there is a force that propels the child forwards. This is not true (despite what it says on the television adverts). It is the lack of a force to stop her that causes the child to keep on moving.

Question	Answer	Mark
(iii)	The crumpling of the car increases the stopping time.	1
	So the deceleration is less.	1
	Hence a smaller force is needed to decelerate the occupants.	1

Examiner's tip Seat belts, crumple zones and air bags all increase the driver's stopping time, causing a smaller deceleration and a smaller force.

Question	Answer	Mark
8 (a)	Knowledge of formula pressure = force ÷ area	**1**
	= 100 N ÷ 5 cm^2	**1**
	= 20 N cm^{-2}	**1**

Examiner's tip N/cm^2 is an alternative to N cm^{-2}. If you converted the area to m^2 the correct answer is 200 000 Pa.

Question	Answer	Mark
(b)	20 N cm^{-2}	**1**
(c)	Force = pressure × area = 20 N cm^{-2} × 25 cm^2	**1**
	= 500 N	**1**

4 LIGHT AND SOUND

Question	Answer	Mark
1 (a) (i)	The loudspeaker cone vibrates in and out.	**1**
	It does 200 complete vibrations each second.	**1**
(ii)	The sketches should show the air molecule move to one side	**1**
	then back to the original position	**1**
	then to the other side	**1**
	and finally back to the original position.	**1**
	This is shown in the following series of diagrams:	

●

→●

●←

●←

→●

Question	Answer	Mark
(b) (i)	The graph should show the amplitude of the wave is reduced.	**1**
	But the time to complete one cycle remains the same.	**1**

Examiner's tip These graphs can be difficult to draw precisely. Use pencil dots to mark in the positions of the top and bottom of the wave as well as any points where it crosses the time axis; then draw the curve.

Question	Answer	Mark
(ii)	The amplitude stays the same.	**1**
	One cycle is completed in half the time.	**1**

Examiner's tip This could also be shown by drawing two complete cycles in the original time for one cycle.

Question	Answer	Mark
(c)	Knowledge of the formula wavelength = speed ÷ frequency	**1**
	= 330 m/s ÷ 200 Hz	**1**
	= 1.65 m	**1**

Examiner's tip Note that the correct answer and unit gain all three marks; if the unit is wrong or missing the third mark is lost.

Question	Answer	Mark
2 (a)	The completed diagrams are shown below. The marks are for:	
	left-hand diagram	
	The wavelength in the glass is reduced.	**1**
	The wavelength increases when the light emerges from the glass.	**1**
	right-hand diagram	
	The wavelength in the glass is reduced.	**1**
	The direction of bending in the glass is correct.	**1**
	The waves leaving the glass are parallel to those that went in.	**1**

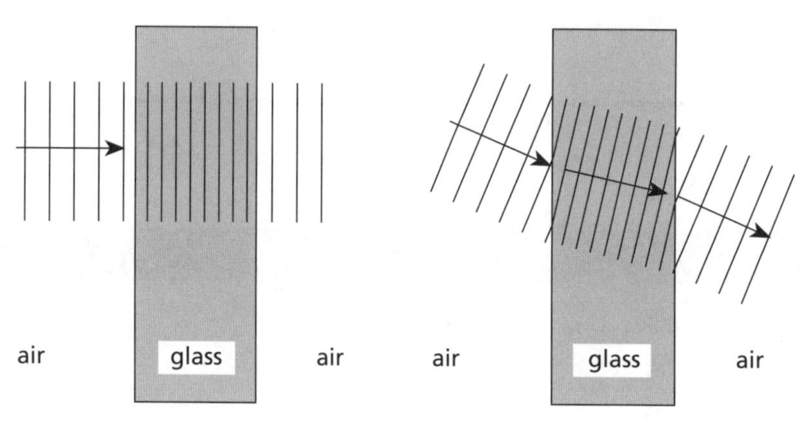

Examiner's tip A common error when drawing the right-hand diagram is to draw the waves in the glass parallel to the sides of the block.

Question	Answer	Mark
(b)	One mark for each ray passing correctly through each prism.	**4**
	The correct diagram is:	

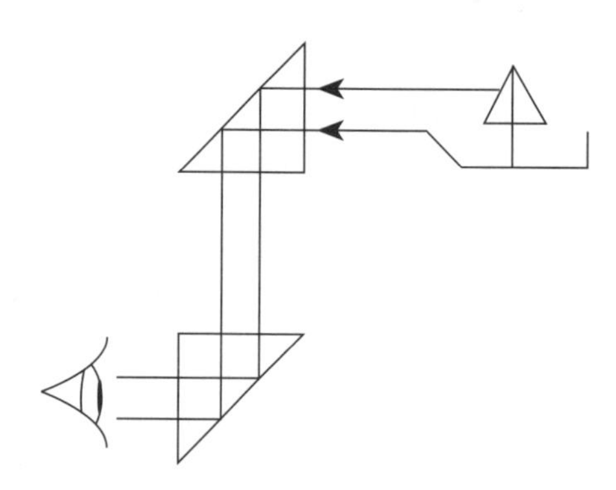

Question	Answer	Mark
3 (a) (i)	Each part of the rope vibrates or oscillates.	**1**
	This movement is at right angles to the direction in which the wave is travelling.	**1**
(ii)	The amplitude is the distance from the centre position to the top of a peak or the bottom of a trough.	**1**
(iii)	One wavelength is the length of one complete cycle, i.e. a peak and a trough.	**1**

Question	Answer	Mark

Examiner's tip The following diagram shows the amplitude (a) and the wavelength (λ).

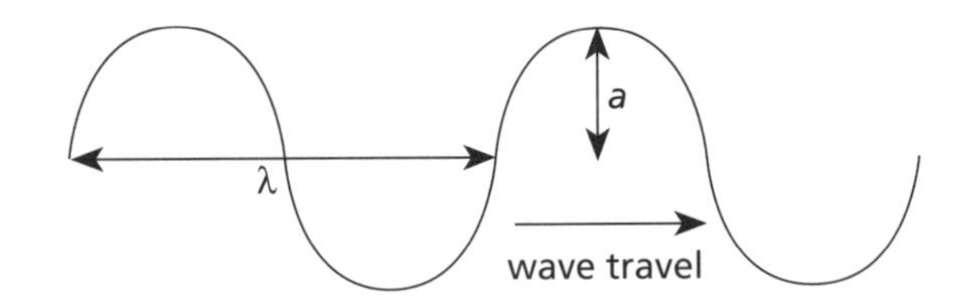

(iv)	Knowledge of formula speed = frequency × wavelength	1
	= 1.5 Hz × 7.5 m	1
	= 11.25 m/s	1

4 (a)	The light comes from the lamp.	1
	It is reflected off the loudspeakers.	1

Examiner's tip All objects that do not give off light of their own are seen because they reflect light from the Sun and other light sources.

(b)	Knowledge of formula wavelength = speed ÷ frequency	1
	= 330m/s ÷ 18 000 Hz	1
	$= 1.83 \times 10^{-2}$ m	1
(c)	The sound has to spread out from the loudspeaker.	1
	Short wavelength waves need to pass through a narrow opening for sufficient spreading by diffraction.	1
	If a large opening were used the sound would not spread throughout the room.	1

Examiner's tip When answering questions on diffraction, you should always make a comparison between the wavelength and the size of the opening that the waves are being diffracted through. It is not enough to state that the opening is 'large' or 'small'.

(d)	Part of the loudspeaker is vibrating with a large amplitude.	1
	This happens when the frequency of the sound being reproduced is equal to the natural frequency of the part producing the 'grating' sound.	2
(e) (i)	Diffraction occurs at the doorway.	1
	This causes the sound to spread out when it passes through.	1

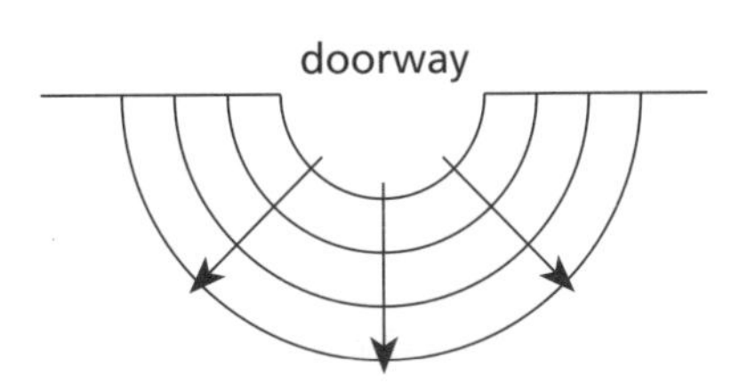

1

Question			Answer	Mark
		(ii)	The light does not spread out when it passes through the doorway.	1
			For light, the doorway is millions of wavelengths wide.	1
			So no diffraction occurs.	1
5	(a)		Knowledge of formula frequency = speed ÷ wavelength	1
			$= 3.0 \times 10^8$ m/s ÷ 0.12 m	1
			$= 2.5 \times 10^9$ Hz	1
	(b)	(i)	Water molecules in the food are vibrating.	1
			The frequency of the microwaves is the same as the frequency of vibration of the water molecules.	1
			This causes increased amplitude of vibration of the water molecules.	1

Examiner's tip This is an example of resonance being used to do a useful job.

Question			Answer	Mark
		(ii)	The water molecules have increased energy.	1
			This energy is passed on to the other molecules in the food.	1

Examiner's tip Temperature or 'hotness' is a measure of the energy that the particles of a substance have.

Question			Answer	Mark
		(iii)	It is not the same as the frequency of the microwaves.	1
6	(a)		When two wave crests or two wave troughs meet they combine to give a wave of increased amplitude.	1
			+ =	1
			Where a wave crest meets a wave trough they combine to give a reduced amplitude.	1
			+ =	1
	(b)		The householder could have a very weak signal.	1
			This would happen if the house was at a place where the waves interfered destructively.	1

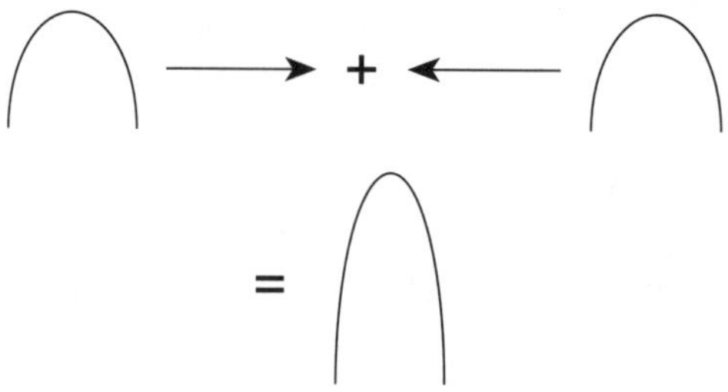

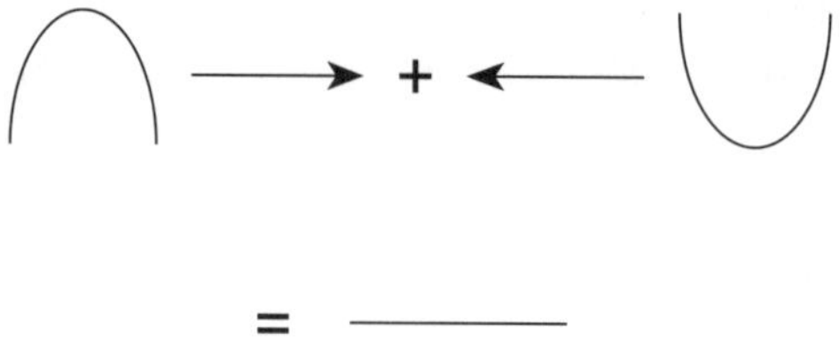

Letts Q&A

Question	Answer	Mark
(c)	In a polarized wave the oscillations are only in one direction.	1
	In horizontal polarization the oscillations are horizontal.	1
	A vertically polarized wave has vertical oscillations.	1

5 THE EARTH'S PLACE IN THE UNIVERSE

Question	Answer	Mark
1 (a) (i)	The craters are due to collisions.	1
	The collisions were with meteorites/rocks.	1

Examiner's tip There was probably a lot of debris around in the Solar System shortly after it was formed.

Question	Answer	Mark
(ii)	Small meteorites would burn up in the planets' atmospheres, therefore not causing impact craters.	1
	Some of those that reached the surface would hit water.	1
	Rain has eroded the craters that were formed.	1
	Wind has also eroded craters.	1
(b) (i)	Mercury has little atmosphere so there is no greenhouse effect to 'trap' energy from the Sun.	1
	The side of the planet facing the Sun will be hot and that facing away will be cold.	1
(ii)	Venus' atmosphere 'traps' energy due to the greenhouse effect.	1
	Venus does not radiate as much energy as Mercury does.	1
(iii)	Venus' atmosphere contains more carbon dioxide than that of the Earth.	1
	So there is a much greater greenhouse effect.	1
(c)	It is similar to that of the Earth.	1
2 (a)	H at the left-hand side of the Earth on the diagram.	1
	H at the right-hand side of the Earth on the diagram.	1
	L at the top of the Earth on the diagram.	1
	L at the bottom of the Earth on the diagram.	1
(b)	The water level first becomes deeper.	1
	Next it gets shallower as X leaves the bulge behind.	1
	Then it becomes deeper and then shallower again.	1
(c)	The Moon is moving anticlockwise in the sense of the diagram.	1
	In one day it moves through approximately 13° of arc.	1

Examiner's tip The Moon orbits the Earth in a period of approximately 28 days, so in 1 day it travels 1/28 of the way around the Earth.

Question			Answer	Mark
3	(a)		The comet speeds up as it approaches the Sun.	1
			This is caused by the increasing gravitational pull.	1
	(b)		The 's' should be at the extreme right-hand side of the comet's orbit on the diagram.	1

Examiner's tip All the time that the comet is travelling away from the Sun, it is slowing down because the gravitational force is pulling it in the 'backwards' direction. It starts to speed up when it changes direction and heads towards the Sun again.

Question			Answer	Mark
	(c)	(i)	Water vapour evaporates from the ice.	1
			This then reflects light from the Sun.	1
		(ii)	The mass decreases when the comet is near the Sun.	1
			The mass stays the same when the comet is distant from the Sun.	1
	(d)		The dust enters the Earth's atmosphere.	1
			Where it burns up as it falls towards the Earth.	1

6 ATOMIC AND MOLECULAR PHYSICS

Question			°Answer	Mark
1	(a)	(i)	The motion of the smoke particle is erratic or random or disorded in direction.	1
			It moves varying distances between changing course.	1
		(ii)	The smoke particle is being hit by things which cannot be seen under a microscope.	1
			The things must therefore be very small.	1
			Given the difference in size, they must be moving very rapidly to make the smoke particle move.	1
			They must also be moving in all directions as there is no pattern to the movement of the smoke particle.	1
	(b)	(i)	Your diagram should show the red colour spreading into the water.	1
			With the density of the redness becoming less further up the beaker.	1
		(ii)	Particles or molecules of dye are knocked off the crystal.	1
			This is done by the bombarding water molecules.	1
			The dye particles spread around in the water, pushed by the 'jostling' water molecules.	1
2	(a)		The same number of molecules are in a smaller volume.	1
			Therefore collisions with the walls are more frequent.	1
			The air is hotter so the molecules are moving faster on average.	1
			Therefore a bigger force is exerted when they collide with the walls.	1

Question	Answer	Mark
(b)	knowledge of the formula $\frac{p_1V_1}{T_1} = \frac{p_2V_2}{T_2}$	1
	rearrange to give $p_2 = \frac{p_1V_1T_2}{T_1V_2}$	1
	$= \frac{100\,\text{kPa} \times 400\,\text{cm}^3 \times 700\,\text{K}}{290\,\text{K} \times 25\,\text{cm}^3}$	1
	$= 3860\,\text{kPa}$	1
3 (a)	Alpha radiation has a short range in air.	1
	It cannot leave the smoke alarm.	1

Examiner's tip Note that it is not true to say that alpha radiation is less harmful than the other types. It has a short range but it is intensely ionizing, and can cause severe damage if it is breathed in.

Question	Answer	Mark
(b)	Electrons are removed when a molecule is ionized.	1
	The current is passed by these electrons moving to the anode.	1
	And by the positive ions (the parts of the atoms left when the electrons have been removed) moving to the cathode.	1
(c)	No the alarm would not work because beta radiation does not cause as much ionization as alpha radiation.	1
	And it is more penetrative, so smoke would not be as effective in reducing the ionization current.	1
(d)	460 years (allow 20 years either way)	2

Examiner's tip It is always wise to calculate the half-life at least twice from a graph as a check.

Question	Answer	Mark
4 (a)	Gamma radiation penetrates body tissue.	1
	Very little is absorbed to damage the patient.	1
(b)	Both would be absorbed by the body tissue.	1
	They would cause ionization and cell damage.	1
	They could also cause gene mutations.	1
(c) (i)	Half-life is the time interval	1
	that it takes for the rate of decay (or the number of undecayed nuclei) to halve.	1

Examiner's tip It is a common misconception that a radioactive source becomes inactive after two half-lives. This is not true, in fact the activity is a quarter of the original activity.

Question	Answer	Mark
(ii)	It remains active long enough to permeate the body and for photographs to be taken.	1
	But it is short enough so that the concentration of radioactive material in the patient's body quickly falls to a very low level.	1

7 PHYSICS AND THE ATMOSPHERE

Question			Answer	Mark
1	(a)	(i)	The water is absorbing energy from the Sun. The warmed water is warming the air. Water is evaporating from the water. The warm, humid air is rising.	3

Examiner's tip Not many candidates would describe all four things and so there is one mark for each correct point made with a maximum mark of 3.

Question			Answer	Mark
		(ii)	The air has cooled as it rose.	1
			Condensation has occurred.	1
			The water is in the form of small droplets.	1
		(iii)	The clouds have risen as they moved over the land mass.	1
			This has caused further cooling and condensation.	1
			The larger water drops that form are falling as rain.	1
	(b)		The Sun is the energy source.	1

Examiner's tip You should be aware that the Sun is the source of almost all the Earth's energy.

Question		Answer	Mark
2	(a)	Energy from the Sun heats the ground.	1
		The warm ground heats the air just above it.	1
		This warm air rises and heats the base of the cloud.	1
	(b)	As the water drops rise they cool.	1
		Freezing occurs when the temperature drops below 0 °C.	1
	(c)	Water vapour condenses on the cold frozen water.	1
		This forms a layer of water on the outside.	1
	(d)	When they fall in the cloud they gather water which freezes as they rise.	1
		Each circulation in the cloud forms an extra layer of ice.	1

Question		Answer	Mark
3	(a)	Fuel burning	1
		Oxidation	1
		Weathering	1
		Respiration	1
		Volcanos	1
	(b)	Plant photosynthesis	1
		Absorption by the oceans	1
	(c)	The algae photosynthesized.	1
		This absorbed carbon dioxide.	1
		And released oxygen into the atmosphere.	1
	(d)	Plants absorb carbon dioxide as they photosynthesize.	1
		Animals produce carbon dioxide by respiration.	1